Contents

Objectives

Atoms, elements and isotopes

When you have completed the work for this Unit, you should be able to:

1 Define correctly, or recognize the best definitions of, or distinguish between true and false statements concerning, all the terms, concepts and principles listed in column 3 of Table A, p. 9.

2 Show that you comprehend the definitions of the terms above by, for example:

(a) making a précis in simpler language of a technical communication involving the terms;

(b) distinguishing among warranted, unwarranted or contradictory conclusions from data involving use of the term;

(c) drawing conclusions, or predicting consequences, from data involving use of the terms.

3 Explain simply, or recognize correct reasons for, the high density of nuclear matter compared with atomic matter in terms of nuclear and atomic dimensions.

4 Explain in elementary terms, or recognize correct reasons for, the fact that chemical behaviour depends on atomic number.

5 Balance simple chemical equations.

6 Give the names of, or select from a given list, the three most abundant elements of the Earth's crust and atmosphere and the three most common substances in the Earth's atmosphere.

7 State how many neutrons and protons there are in a nuclide for which you are given the symbol.

8 Draw a simple labelled diagram illustrating the basic principles of operation of a mass spectrometer.

9 Indicate the nuclide produced from a given nuclide by a specified radioactive decay process, using the table of elements in Appendix 1.

10 Draw a diagram to illustrate the phenomenon of dispersion of light.

11 Use a spectroscope to identify atomic spectra generated in a flame and determine the composition of a given sample given the appropriate atomic spectra.

12 Distinguish between emission and absorption spectra by describing or selecting or drawing diagrams.

13 Explain briefly the origin of atomic spectra in terms of energy jumps.

14 Draw an energy-level diagram, given a simple atomic spectrum calibrated in hertz.

15 Draw an atomic spectrum (in hertz), given an energy-level diagram calibrated in joule.

16 Show electron 'jumps' by arrows on an energy-level diagram for either absorption or emission spectra.

17 Show diagrammatically the ionization potential on an energy-level diagram.

18 Determine graphically an ionization potential, given the energy-level diagram.

The Open University

Science Foundation Course Unit 6

ATOMS, ELEMENTS AND ISOTOPES: ATOMIC STRUCTURE

Prepared by the Science Foundation Course Team

THE OPEN UNIVERSITY

A NOTE ABOUT AUTHORSHIP OF THIS TEXT

This text is one of a series that, together, constitutes *a component part* of the Science Foundation Course. The other components are a series of television and radio programmes, home experiments and a summer school.

The course has been produced by a team, which accepts responsibility for the course as a whole and for each of its components.

THE SCIENCE FOUNDATION COURSE TEAM

M. J. Pentz (Chairman and General Editor)

F. Aprahamian	(Editor)	A. R. Kaye	(Educational Technology)
A. Clow	(BBC)	J. McCloy	(BBC)
P. A. Crompton	(BBC)	J. E. Pearson	(Editor)
G. F. Elliott	(Physics)	S. P. R. Rose	(Biology)
G. C. Fletcher	(Physics)	R. A. Ross	(Chemistry)
I. G. Gass	(Earth Sciences)	P. J. Smith	(Earth Sciences)
L. J. Haynes	(Chemistry)	F. R. Stannard	(Physics)
R. R. Hill	(Chemistry)	J. Stevenson	(BBC)
R. M. Holmes	(Biology)	N. A. Taylor	(BBC)
S. W. Hurry	(Biology)	M. E. Varley	(Biology)
D. A. Johnson	(Chemistry)	A. J. Walton	(Physics)
A. B. Jolly	(BBC)	B. G. Whatley	(BBC)
R. Jones	(BBC)	R. C. L. Wilson	(Earth Sciences)

The following people acted as consultants for certain components of the course:

J. D. Beckman	R. J. Knight	J. R. Ravetz
B. S. Cox	D. J. Miller	H. Rose
G. Davies	M. W. Neil	
G. Holister	C. Newey	

The Open University Press Limited
Walton Hall, Bletchley, Bucks

First Published 1971
Copyright © 1971 The Open University

Designed by The Media Development Group of the Open University

Printed in Great Britain by
Oxley Press Ltd,
London and Edinburgh

SBN 335 02002 X

Open University courses provide a method of study for independent learners through an integrated teaching system, including textual material, radio and television programmes and short residential courses. This text is one of a series that make up the correspondence element of the Science Foundation Course.

The Open University's courses represent a new system of university level education. Much of the teaching material is still in a developmental stage. Courses and course materials are, therefore, kept continually under revision. It is intended to issue regular up-dating notes as and when the need arises, and new editions will be brought out when necessary.

Further information on Open University courses may be obtained from The Admissions Office, The Open University, P.O. Box 48, Bletchley, Buckinghamshire.

19   Calculate (using long hand or log tables, or any other appropriate device) to a given degree of precision:

(a) the relative quantities of initial and final compounds, given a chemical equation and a table of relative atomic masses;

(b) relative atomic masses from percentage compositions of compounds of known formulae;

(c) formulae of compounds, given a table of relative atomic masses and the percentage composition of the elements in the compounds;

(d) the number of atoms in a given mass of an element, given the relative atomic mass of the element and the mass in kg of a ^{12}C atom;

(e) the relative atomic mass of an isotope mixture, given the relative atomic masses and the percentage abundances of the components of the mixture;

(f) the energy of photons of light of a given frequency;

(g) the frequencies of light with photons of given energies.

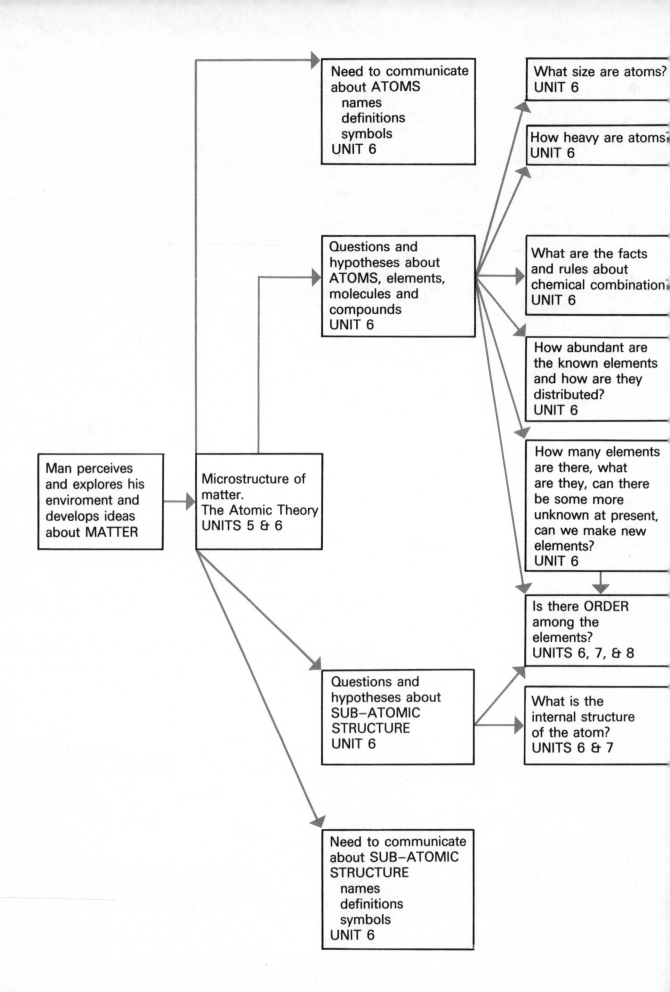

Need to communicate about ATOMS
names
definitions
symbols
UNIT 6

What size are atoms?
UNIT 6

How heavy are atoms?
UNIT 6

Questions and hypotheses about ATOMS, elements, molecules and compounds
UNIT 6

What are the facts and rules about chemical combination?
UNIT 6

How abundant are the known elements and how are they distributed?
UNIT 6

Man perceives and explores his enviroment and develops ideas about MATTER

Microstructure of matter.
The Atomic Theory
UNITS 5 & 6

How many elements are there, what are they, can there be some more unknown at present, can we make new elements?
UNIT 6

Is there ORDER among the elements?
UNITS 6, 7, & 8

Questions and hypotheses about SUB–ATOMIC STRUCTURE
UNIT 6

What is the internal structure of the atom?
UNITS 6 & 7

Need to communicate about SUB–ATOMIC STRUCTURE
names
definitions
symbols
UNIT 6

Conceptual diagram covering Units 6, 7 and 8

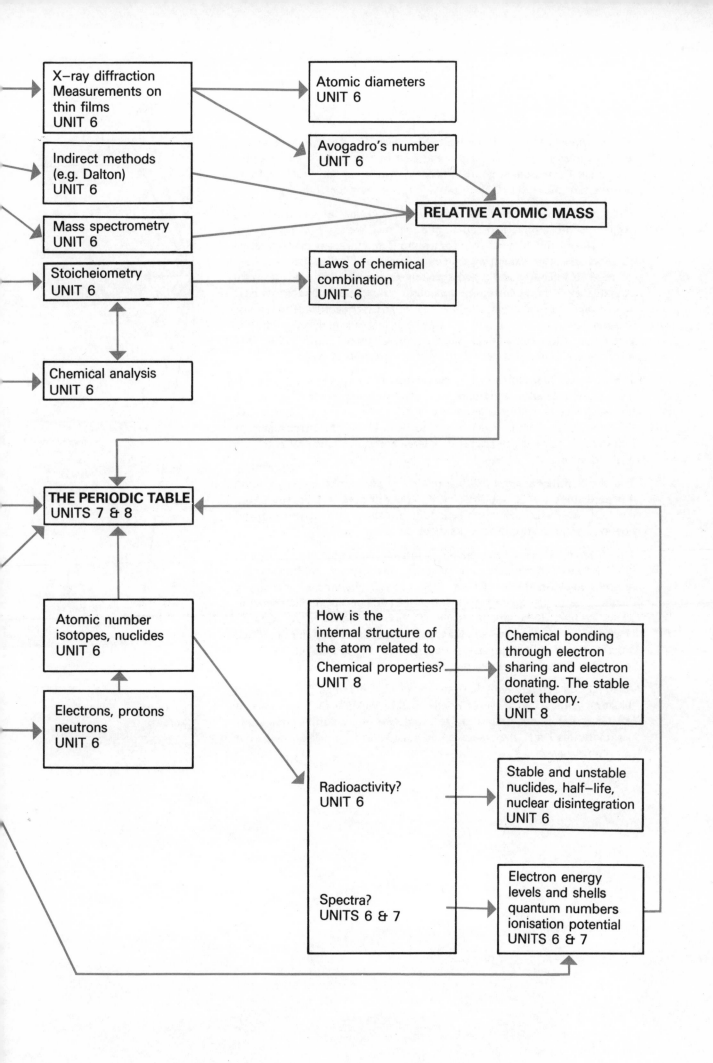

Study Guide

A basic understanding of contemporary views on the nature of matter and its transformations is an essential part of any scientist's intellectual equipment for reasons which will become evident as our course unfolds. It is the purpose of this Unit to provide this basic understanding.

The Unit takes up the story of force, energy and the states of matter and extends it into atomic and sub-atomic regions. We explore the basis of atomic theory and discuss how it comes about that there are many different elements in nature exhibiting equally diverse chemical properties. Since we need to refer frequently and precisely to the elements and the compounds they form, we introduce the notation for these that scientists have agreed on. The fundamental importance of *measurement* leads to a study of atomic mass and to quantitative aspects of the ways in which atoms join together to form compounds. Simple expressions for basic quantitative relationships in chemistry are dealt with in Appendix 2, p. 47.

The postulate that atoms can be subdivided is an epoch-making one. It leads us to a detailed study of aspects of electromagnetic radiations and how such studies enable us to make deductions about the arrangement of the electrons in an atom with respect to its nucleus. This arrangement is important because it determines to a large extent the chemical reactivity of the elements.

This seems rather a heavy load for one study unit, and there is no use in our pretending that it is all easy stuff. You will need to plan your work carefully. The usual self-assessment tests are there to help you find out how well you are grasping the points made.

The order in which subject matter is introduced is that which appears 'logical' to us as communicators. However, this may well not be the order in which you wish to study. Choose the sections in any order your curiosity dictates, but be prepared to meet with terms and concepts in later sections which are likely to be unfamiliar unless you have studied earlier sections. One word of warning here—do make certain you have read the Broadcast Notes (TV and radio) and have at least glanced through the other sections referred to before transmission.

As in all Units so far, study both the list of objectives and the conceptual diagram of the Unit, however briefly, before tackling the main part of the Unit. Refer back frequently to these two items during your study period on this Unit—they represent a framework on which to hang your new knowledge.

Table A

A List of Scientific Terms, Concepts and Principles used in Unit 6

Taken as pre-requisite			Introduced in this Unit			
1	**2**		**3**		**4**	
Assumed from general knowledge	Introduced in a previous Unit	Unit No.	Developed in this Unit	Page No.	Developed in a later Unit	Unit No.
vacuum	atom	5	electron	13	chemical bond	8
conduction of electricity	molecule	5	alpha particle	14	crystal structure	8
percentage	fluorescent screen	2	atomic nucleus	15	electromagnetic field	23
±	mass	2	atomic number	15	nucleon	31
arc of circle	nuclear forces	4	neutron	15	electron transfer	8
radius of curvature	coulomb	4	proton	15	electron sharing	8
focus	photographic plate	2	chemical symbol	16	uniform magnetic field	22
unstable	graph	MAFS	compound	16	ion	9
amplify	energy	4	element	16	binding energy	31
	half-life	2	isotope of an element	18	positron	31
	electromagnetic wave	2	mass number	18	diffraction	28
	experimental observation	1, 2	nuclide	18		
	crystalline	5	atomic mass unit	19		
	electric charge	4	deuterium	19		
	negative charge	4	protium	19		
	positive charge	4	relative atomic mass	19		
	electrically neutral	4	tritium	19		
	electric field	4	Avogadro's number	20		
	electrical current	4	mole	20		
			mass spectrometer	22		
			mass defect	25		
			beta particle	26		
			gamma-radiation	26		
			radioactivity	26		
			curie	27		
			Geiger counter	27		
			specific activity	27		
			dispersion of light	30		
			refraction	30		
			continuous spectrum	31		
			photon	31		
			Planck's constant	31		
			solar spectrum	31		
			atomic spectra	32		
			emission spectra	32		
			line spectra	32		
			absorption spectra	33		
			energy-level diagram	37		
			ground state energy level	37		
			principal quantum number	40		
			quantum numbers	40		
			ionization energy	42		
			molecular formula	47		

Introduction

The general aims of this Unit and of Unit 7 are:

(i) to outline current views on the atomic structure of matter and on the structure of atoms;

(ii) to develop the concepts of atomic number, element, nuclides, isotope and relative atomic mass from the concept of the nuclear atom;

(iii) to discuss the evidence leading to the electronic structure of elements and to show how this leads to a periodicity in structure and thus provides a theoretical basis for the Periodic Table.

We shall discuss some of the historical background to the development of ideas of atomic structure in the radio programme associated with Unit 6. The television programme will be on the determination of the charge on the electron by Millikan's method, and the use of the mass spectrometer in the determination of relative atomic mass.

Background reading

We assume that you are familiar with the ideas and concepts discussed in Units 2, 4 and 5 especially.

Parallel reading*

The Origins and Growth of Physical Science, Volume 2 (edited by D. L. Hurd and J. J. Kipling, Penguin Books, 1964), contains extensive quotations from the original publications of Dalton, Gay-Lussac, Avogadro, Mendeleev, J. J. Thomson, Becquerel, Rutherford and others whose work has provided the foundations on which the present theory of atomic structure is built. It also includes brief but invaluable introductory accounts which show the significance of the work described in the publications and set this work in perspective.

Questions in the text

Scattered through the text you will find a number of questions. You should try to answer these questions whenever you come to them. Sometimes the answer to the question will be found immediately in the margin; sometimes a note in the margin will direct you to the back of the Unit, where the answer will be found; sometimes the question will be answered in the subsequent main text.

* *This is recommended* background *reading for those who have the time. It is not obligatory ('white-page') set reading.*

6.1 The Elementary Structure of the Atom

6.1.1 The atomic structure of matter

In previous Units we have explored forces and energy and the states of matter: we are now going to consider the nature of matter and its transformations. As you saw in Unit 5 the keystone of present-day views on the structure of matter is the atomic theory, which holds that matter is composed of vast numbers of very small particles called *atoms*: this theory was put on a quantitative basis by John Dalton (1766–1844) in the first few years of the nineteenth century. A discussion of Dalton's work will be the main theme of the radio programme. In this Unit, however, we will present the current picture as our starting point and show how it rationalizes and interprets some of the experimental observations which have been made since man first began his investigations of the world around him.

atoms

6.1.2 The size of atoms

We have said that atoms are very small, but just how small are they? This is not an easy question to answer—the modern theory of the structure of the atom suggests that the atom should not be pictured as a body with a sharp boundary, so that to measure the dimensions of an atom would be comparable to measuring the dimensions of a cloud where the first difficulty would be to decide where the cloud began. We can, however, consider an 'effective size' for an atom. Atoms combine together in molecules or pack together as solids at definite distances from one another, the distances varying slightly with circumstances. These distances can be determined and so give a measure of an effective size of the atom. Knowledge of such effective sizes serves, as we shall see later, to give us information on the nature of chemical bonds, crystal structure and the properties of matter generally.

If it is assumed that atoms are contained in a spherical volume, methods can then be devised to measure how closely the centres of these spheres can approach one another and this will give an atomic 'diameter'. This 'diameter' is found to lie between 0.7 and 6 Å.*

atomic diameter

The most powerful method for determining such atomic 'diameters' involves the interpretation of the ways in which X-rays are diffracted by crystalline materials, but a relatively simple experiment which gives some indication of atomic dimensions may be considered briefly here.

You have probably noticed the iridescent patterns which develop when a drop of oil or petrol falls on to a wet road and is allowed to spread. Suppose you were to take a known volume of oil and allow it to spread to its maximum extent, as a continuous film, on the surface of a pool of water. If you were then to measure the area of the film, you could calculate the thickness of the film because you would know the original volume. At its maximum extent the film would be found to be about 10 Å thick. Of course,

---

* 1 *ångström unit* = 1 $\mathring{A}$ = 10^{-10} *m.*
The ångström unit is not an officially recognized SI unit but is convenient to use because most interatomic and intermolecular distances lie between 1 and 10 $\mathring{A}$.

this would not be a film of *atoms* spread on the water; it would be, as we shall see later, a film of oil *molecules*, but the important information that this simple experiment would have given you would be that the atoms which make up these molecules would be contained in a sphere with a diameter of *less than 10 Å*.

If the film is about 10 Å thick, why do we say that the atoms in the oil would be contained in a sphere of *less* than 10 Å?

If you are unsure of your answer to this question, re-read the last sentence of the paragraph noting carefully that the film consists of oil *molecules*: molecules are made of atoms and atoms must therefore be smaller than molecules. Note also that there may be *more* than one molecular layer in the thickness of the film.

6.1.3 The structure of atoms

In spite of their small size, atoms have a complex internal structure which we need to consider in order to understand something of how atoms react with one another.

Atoms, although they are electrically neutral overall, consist of a central nucleus which is positively charged and electrons which are negatively charged. The evidence for this was gathered together in the period from 1890–1910 by three main groups of workers led by J. J. Thomson, R. A. Millikan and E. Rutherford respectively.

J. J. Thomson, in a very famous series of experiments investigating the conduction of electricity through a vacuum, was able to show that a large number of negative particles are emitted from a piece of metal heated in a vacuum. By a clever application of electromagnetic fields (which you will learn more about in Unit 23), Thomson was able to measure the ratio of the charge of the particles to their mass.* These particles, which are called electrons, were also studied by Millikan. In a famous experiment (see this Unit's TV programme), Millikan measured the electric charges on oil drops and found that the drops acquired charges which were exact multiples of a basic charge, which he called the electronic charge. This negative electronic charge had the same value as the positive charge on a hydrogen atom which had lost its electron: a value of 1.6×10^{-19} coulomb. This value, taken with Thomson's measurement of the charge/mass ratio, gave the electronic mass as only 1/1837th part of the mass of the hydrogen atom.

electrons

Thus, Thomson and Millikan identified a particle, the electron, that was very much less massive than the whole atom but carried the same amount of charge (though opposite sign) as an atom that lacked an electron. We shall not at this point study the different chemical elements in terms of the different number of electrons which they possess.

We pose to you the question which Thomson posed himself; how do you think the matter is arranged within the atom?

Thomson supposed that the positive part of the atom, having almost all the total mass of that atom, was distributed over the total size of the atom as a sort of continuum of positive charge in which the electrons existed like plums in a plum-pudding. This was Thomson's 'plum-pudding model'.

---

* *The 'beam-tube' apparatus such as Thomson used is briefly shown in this Unit's TV programme.*

Given the known charge and weight of the electrons and the fact that atoms as a whole were electrically neutral, and many times heavier than an electron, the plum-pudding model was reasonable and was accepted for some years. It was overthrown effectively by the results of a single experiment in physics, the alpha-scattering experiment of Rutherford, Geiger and Marsden. Rutherford and his colleagues were using a conveniently available atomic probe, a small piece of radium at the bottom of a hole in a piece of lead. Radium emits particles which are called alpha particles (this is an example of radioactive decay, see Unit 2 and this Unit section 6.3). Alpha particles are, as it happens, atoms of helium (the second element, see section 6.3.1) that have lost their two electrons. They are positively charged and are shot out by the radium at a high velocity. Rutherford and his colleagues shot this beam of particles through a very thin gold foil. They observed the scattered particles on a fluorescent screen. Figure 1 shows a schematic diagram of the Rutherford scattering experiment.

alpha particles

What do you expect to happen to the beam of alpha particles?

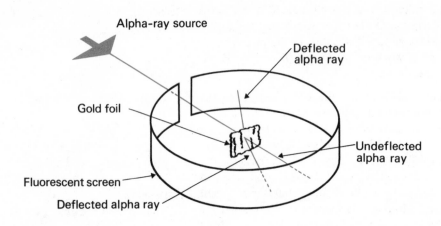

Figure 1

The Rutherford alpha ray scattering experiment.

Rutherford and his colleagues supposed that the effect of the thin gold foil on the positively charged alpha particles traversing it would be to spread the beam out slightly. They found to their surprise that some of the bombarding particles were shot back towards the bombarding source. This was completely inexplicable on the then accepted Thomson plum-pudding atom model. On that model, there was no reason why any electric field within the atom should be sufficiently intense to repel any of the bombarding alpha particles so violently. Rutherford thought that this experimental result was almost unbelievable. In his own words, 'It was almost as incredible as if you fired a 15-inch shell at a piece of tissue paper and it came back and hit you'. He quickly realized that the only way to account for these large deflections was to suppose that the positive electric charge and mass in a metal foil were concentrated in very small regions. Then, although most of the alpha particles would go through the metal without much deflection, occasionally an alpha particle would come close to the high concentration of positive charge. This high concentration of positive charge would be essentially immovable because of its high mass. As the like charges got closer they would repel each other (Units 2 and 4) and the repulsion could be big enough to cause the alpha particle to swerve violently from its original path. Thus Rutherford was driven to suggest the nuclear atom; an atom that has a central nucleus in which the positive charge and mass are concentrated.

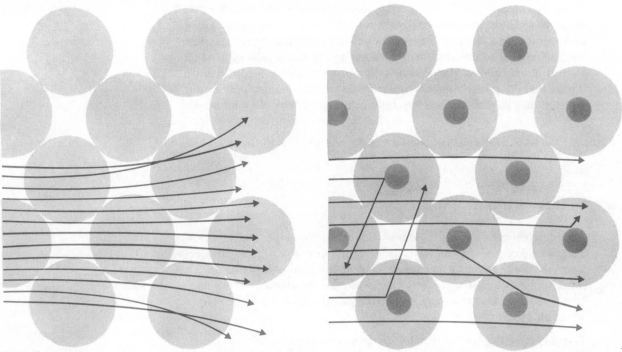

Figure 2

Deflection of alpha rays by gold foil.

(*a*) *Thomson's model of atoms. According to this model in which the positive charge of each atom is uniformly distributed, alpha particles passing through the medium would not deviate substantially from their original path.*

(*b*) *Rutherford's model of atoms. The positive charge of each atom is concentrated into a small volume with the result that alpha particles passing close by are scattered through a large angle.*

Rutherford's experiment suggested that the nucleus of the atom was some 10^5 times smaller than the diameter of the atom itself, that is the nuclear size is approximately 10^{-15} m compared to the atomic size of 10^{-10} m. To give an analogy, if an atom were magnified so that the nucleus was the size of a full-stop, then the whole atom would be bigger than a house. This house would contain the electrons of the atom; we shall later come to consider, in fair detail, in what manner these electrons fill the house.

Since the nucleus accounts for nearly all the mass of the atom but for only 10^{-15} of the volume of the atom, it follows that the density of the nucleus is enormous, about 3×10^{12} times that of lead. You may wonder whether matter of such extreme density will behave like ordinary matter. You will see later, in Unit 31, that it does not.

atomic nucleus

6.1.4 The nucleus—protons, neutrons; atomic number

The nucleus can be regarded simply as being composed of two different types of particle of almost equal mass: *protons* which are positively charged, and *neutrons* which are neutral. These particles are known collectively as *nucleons*. The forces which hold these particles in the nucleus—nuclear forces—have been described briefly in Unit 4 and an account of the structure of the nucleus will be given in Unit 31. The nucleus of the hydrogen atom, which is the lightest atom, consists of a single proton. Usually the number of neutrons in the nucleus of an atom is roughly the same as the number of protons, but the ratio of neutrons to protons increases slowly as the number of protons increases.

proton
neutron
nucleon

The mass of an electron is only 1/1836th of that of a proton. Its electrical charge is, however, equal to that of a proton although of opposite sign. (As has been shown in section 6.1.3 this charge is 1.6×10^{-19} coulombs.) Since atoms are electrically neutral, the number of electrons and the number of protons in an atom must be the same. This number, which ranges from 1 (hydrogen) to 105 (an element as yet unnamed) is known as the *atomic number Z*.

atomic number

15

Chemists are interested in the ways in which atoms combine with other atoms to form compounds—the chemical behaviour of the atom—as we shall see in Unit 8. This combination of atoms takes place by processes of electron transfer or electron sharing, and so the chemical behaviour of an atom is determined to a very large extent by its electrons. From this we can see that the atomic number—which determines the number of electrons in the atom—in effect defines the *chemical* characteristics of an atom.

What, therefore, can we say about the chemical behaviour of atoms which have the same atomic number?

6.1.5   Elements and chemical symbols

All atoms which have the same atomic number will have the same chemical behaviour (because they all have the same number of extranuclear electrons on which chemical behaviour depends), and this leads us to the concept of an *element* as *a substance in which all the atoms have the same atomic number*. Elements may be regarded as the basic substances from which all matter is formed. element

This fundamental importance of elements was emphasized in earlier definitions of the type 'a substance which cannot be decomposed by chemical reaction into substances of simpler composition'. Such definitions are unsatisfactory, partly because of their negative nature (i.e. they define something which *cannot* be done), and partly because of the difficulty of defining terms like 'chemical reaction'. But the concept of elements as the basic units from which all matter is made is fundamental.

By 1970, 105 different elements were known, with atomic numbers 1–105 inclusive. Of these about 90 were found in nature, the remainder, including all those with $Z > 92$, have been made in the laboratory by *nuclear reactions*. These are reactions which involve the nucleus of an atom as distinct from chemical reactions which involve the extranuclear electrons of an atom.

A list of elements showing their atomic numbers is given in Appendix 1. The list also gives the *chemical symbol* for an atom of each element. These chemical symbol symbols are usually initial letters; thus C represents an atom of carbon and Fe represents an atom of iron (Latin, *ferrum*). Such symbols are also loosely used to represent the element in general rather than just one atom of the element.

Two or more elements can combine together to form a *compound*. A com- compound pound has a definite composition no matter how it is prepared. For example, water always consists of hydrogen and oxygen combined in the ratio 1.008 to 8 by weight no matter by what method it is prepared* (see Appendix 2). As you can imagine, the 105 elements can give rise to an immense number of compounds. Probably 4 million compounds are currently known and the number of possible compounds, although not limitless, is very large.

Although some elements occur on Earth in the free state, that is uncombined with other elements (examples are helium, oxygen, nitrogen, gold, copper and carbon), most elements occur in combination with one another.

---

* *Assuming that the proportions of isotopes remain constant (see section 6.2.2).*

6.1.6 The relative abundance of elements

The table below gives the estimated percentage composition (by mass) of the Earth's surface, land and sea, and atmosphere:

Oxygen	49.2
Silicon	25.7
Aluminium	7.5
Iron	4.7
Calcium	3.4
Sodium	2.8
Potassium	2.6
Magnesium	1.9
Hydrogen	0.9

You are *not* expected to remember these numbers, though you should, at least, remember which three elements are the most abundant ones in the Earth's crust and which three in the atmosphere.

These nine elements make up almost 99 per cent of the total. The large amount of oxygen is immediately striking. The other major element is silicon, and many rocks of the Earth's surface are compounds of silicon, oxygen and one or more of the other elements on the list. Such compounds are called silicates of aluminium, iron, calcium, magnesium, etc.

Other points that the table reveals are that many of the familiar elements which play an important part in economic life, in fact make up only a very small part of the Earth's surface. For example, carbon, which as we will see later is an element present in all living matter, plant and animal, as well as in chalk, limestone and coal, does not appear—its estimated abundance is 0.02 per cent—nor do nitrogen, copper or tin, all of which are even less abundant than carbon.

The atmosphere consists mainly of nitrogen (75 per cent by weight) and oxygen (23 per cent) with small quantities of argon (1.2 per cent), carbon dioxide (0.75 per cent) and traces of neon, helium, methane, krypton, nitrous oxide, hydrogen, ozone and xenon. In addition the air usually contains between 1 and 4 per cent water vapour (by volume). Of course, in large cities and heavily industrialized areas atmospheric pollution will change some of these figures; the percentage of carbon dioxide rises, and other gases, such as sulphur dioxide, carbon monoxide and nitrogen dioxide, can be detected. (We will be discussing this further in Unit 34.)

6.2 Isotopes and Atomic Mass

6.2.1 Nuclides

You will remember that we defined an element as a substance in which all the atoms have the same atomic number, i.e. all the atoms have the same number of protons in the nucleus.

Does this mean that all the atoms in an element are necessarily identical in *every* respect (including their masses)?

In this definition of an element we said nothing about the number of neutrons in the nucleus because the chemical behaviour of the atoms concerned, being dependent on the number of extranuclear electrons in the atom and hence on the number of protons and the atomic number, is virtually independent of the number of neutrons. That is to say, in our definition of an element we had in mind the basic idea of a substance, all the components of which showed the same chemical behaviour.

It is, however, useful to have a name for substances in which all the atoms have the same atomic number *and* also have the same number of neutrons in their *nuclei*, and we call such substances *nuclides*. About 1600 nuclides are known.

nuclide

6.2.2 Isotopes of elements

You have seen from the discussion above that atoms which have the same atomic number, that is, atoms of the same element, can nevertheless have different masses because their nuclei contain different numbers of neutrons. Atoms of the same element which so differ in their masses are called *isotopes* of that element. In other words, the isotopes of an element are a set of nuclides with the same atomic number.

isotope

For example, the element hydrogen has atomic number 1 (that is, it has one nuclear proton and one electron) and exists as three different isotopes in which the nucleus has 0, 1 and 2 neutrons respectively.

If you wish to refer to a particular isotope of any element (that is to a particular nuclide), the symbol for an atom of the element can be expanded by writing a superscript which shows the total number of neutrons plus protons (the *mass number* A) and a subscript which shows the number of protons (the atomic number Z). Thus the three isotopes of hydrogen mentioned above can be symbolized as:

mass number

$$\mathrm{{}^{1}_{1}H} \qquad \mathrm{{}^{2}_{1}H} \qquad \mathrm{{}^{3}_{1}H}$$

Each has one proton in the nucleus, shown by the subscript figure. The second isotope also has one neutron in the nucleus, giving it a mass number of 2, shown in the superscript.* The third isotope has two neutrons in the nucleus, giving it a mass number of 3. The element carbon has three isotopes which similarly can be symbolized as:

$$\mathrm{{}^{12}_{6}C} \qquad \mathrm{{}^{13}_{6}C} \qquad \mathrm{{}^{14}_{6}C}$$

* *The symbols given are agreed by international convention. In some books, especially American, the practice has been to write these symbols with the mass number superscript written after the symbol for the element, thus:* $\mathrm{{}_{1}H^{1}}$ $\mathrm{{}_{1}H^{2}}$ $\mathrm{{}_{1}H^{3}}$

How many neutrons are there in each of these three isotopes of carbon?

If you are unsure of your answer, read the preceding section again; remember that the superscript number is the mass number and the subscript figure is the atomic number.

See Answer 1, p. 62.

As you have seen, the atomic number defines the element under consideration; it is therefore normally unnecessary to specify both the atomic number *and* the symbol of the element. Accordingly, it is usual to omit the atomic number subscript; thus $^{14}_{6}C$ is usually written ^{14}C (and referred to in speech as 'cee-fourteen'). All elements have several isotopes. Some of these isotopes occur naturally, the others have been made in the laboratory by nuclear reactions.

The isotopes of hydrogen are the only nuclides which have been given individual names. The isotope $^{2}_{1}H$ is known as *deuterium* and is commonly given the symbol D. The isotope $^{3}_{1}H$ is similarly known as *tritium*. The isotope $^{1}_{1}H$ is sometimes called *protium*, but is much more commonly referred to merely as hydrogen. This is probably because any given sample of hydrogen (either combined with other elements or as hydrogen gas) normally consists of a mixture of about 6 000 parts of protium to one of deuterium. Tritium, which is made in the laboratory by nuclear reactions, is unstable.

deuterium
tritium
protium

The separation of isotopes is a matter of some difficulty since their chemical properties are identical. Because of this, separation techniques usually depend on those physical methods which are sufficiently sensitive to distinguish the slight differences in relative mass between one isotope and another. In this respect the separation of hydrogen and deuterium is favoured since the deuterium atom has virtually twice the mass of the hydrogen atom.

6.2.3 Relative atomic mass

The masses of atoms of individual nuclides can be expressed as fractions of a gramme. However, it is generally more convenient to consider not the actual mass of an atom but its mass *relative* to that of another atom. For this purpose, the most common isotope of the element carbon, namely $^{12}_{6}C$, is arbitrarily defined as having a mass of exactly 12 *atomic mass units* (a.m.u.) and the atomic masses of all the other elements are then related to this arbitrary standard. As you will see later in discussions of the mass spectrometer, such relative atomic masses can be determined with very high accuracy.

atomic mass unit

Thus, the statement that the relative atomic mass of the nuclide $^{11}_{5}B$ is 11.0 means that an atom of that particular nuclide has a mass of 11/12 of the mass of one atom of the carbon isotope $^{12}_{6}C$. (You will notice that the *relative* atomic mass is expressed as a number: alternatively, it could be said that the atomic mass of $^{11}_{5}B$ is 11.0 atomic mass units, an atomic mass unit being defined so that the mass of an atom of the carbon isotope $^{12}_{6}C$ is exactly 12 atomic mass units; 1 a.m.u. is approximately 1.66×10^{-27} kg.)

relative atomic mass

Almost all elements exist in nature as mixtures of isotopes—carbon itself normally occurs as a mixture of three isotopes, the most common one $^{12}_{6}C$ being accompanied by very small amounts of $^{13}_{6}C$ and $^{14}_{6}C$—and these isotopes will of course have different atomic masses.

Can you remember why isotopes have different relative atomic masses?

If you are unsure of your answer re-read the section on the isotopes of elements.

The relative atomic mass of an element which consists of a mixture of isotopes will therefore be determined by the atomic masses of the isotopes present and their relative amounts. For example, suppose an element consists of a mixture of 90 per cent of an isotope with atomic mass 100 and 10 per cent of an isotope with atomic mass 102. 100 atoms of the element will consist of 90 atoms of atomic mass 100 and 10 atoms of atomic mass 102, the total mass of 100 atoms will therefore be 10 020 and the relative atomic mass of the element will be 100.2.

This can be expressed formally by saying that the *relative atomic mass of an element** is the ratio of the average mass per atom of the natural isotopic composition of an element to 1/12 of the mass of an atom of the nuclide $^{12}_{6}C$.

relative atomic mass

6.2.4 The Avogadro constant: the mole

We have said (section 6.2.3) that 1 a.m.u. is approximately 1.66×10^{-27} kg and that the atomic mass of ^{12}C is by definition 12 a.m.u.

> **Suppose you had exactly 12 g of this carbon isotope, how many atoms would it contain?**

The mass of one atom would be $12 \times 1.66 \times 10^{-27}$ kg and so 1 kg of the carbon isotope would contain $1/(12 \times 1.66 \times 10^{-27})$ atoms and 12 g would contain $12/(12 \times 1.66 \times 10^{-27} \times 10^{3}) = 6.02 \times 10^{23}$ atoms.

This number, the number of atoms of the ^{12}C isotope in exactly 12 g of ^{12}C, is known as *Avogadro's number* or *Avogadro's constant*, N_A. It is an important constant because it leads us to the unit known as a *mole*. A mole of any substance is that amount of substance which contains as many particles (atoms, molecules, ions or any other particle) as there are atoms of ^{12}C in exactly 12 g of ^{12}C. In other words, one mole of any substance contains Avogadro's number of particles of that substance.

Avogadro's number
mole

Thus the mole of iron (relative atomic mass 55.847) will contain Avogadro's number of iron atoms and will have a mass of 55.847 g. Similarly, a mole of carbon dioxide, CO_2, will contain Avogadro's number of carbon dioxide molecules and will have a mass of 43.999 g (because the sum of the relative atomic masses of one carbon atom and two oxygen atoms is 43.999).

A mole is a convenient unit to use when we are considering the quantitative relationships between reactants and products in any chemical reaction (see Appendix 2).

6.2.5 The determination of relative atomic mass: the mass spectrometer

The relative atomic mass of an element can be determined in two main ways. The first way depends on the fact that atomic mass is related to the atomic mass of the carbon isotope $^{12}_{6}C$ which, by definition, is exactly 12 a.m.u. If it can be determined what mass of a particular element will combine with 12 g of that carbon isotope then, provided the relative numbers of the atoms of the two elements in the compound formed are known, a direct determination of the relative atomic mass of the element can be made.

For example,** suppose you wanted to determine the relative atomic mass of oxygen. Oxygen and carbon combine to form a compound, carbon

---

* *This expression replaces the term* atomic weight of an element *used in earlier literature and some textbooks.*

** *In these examples for simplicity we will assume that ordinary (naturally occurring) carbon has a relative atomic mass of* 12.

monoxide, each molecule of which contains one atom of carbon and one atom of oxygen. Its molecular formula is therefore CO. Suppose you were able to determine that this compound contained 42.8 per cent by mass of carbon and 57.2 per cent by mass of oxygen, what would be the relative atomic mass of oxygen? The calculation is simple, since 42.8 g of carbon combined with 57.2 g of oxygen, 12 g of carbon would combine with $\dfrac{12 \times 57.2}{42.8}$ g $= 16$ g oxygen and hence the relative atomic mass of oxygen must be 16.

Carbon and oxygen also combine together to form another compound called carbon dioxide (CO_2) in a molecule of which there is one atom of carbon and two atoms of oxygen. This compound contains 27.3 per cent of carbon and 72.7 per cent of oxygen, so what is the relative atomic mass of oxygen here? Again, since 27.3 g of carbon combines with 72.7 g of oxygen, 12 g of carbon must combine with $\dfrac{12 \times 72.7}{27.3} = 32$ g oxygen, *but* 32 g oxygen represents 2 atoms of oxygen and hence the relative atomic mass of oxygen is 16.

> **A compound carbon tetrafluoride, CF_4, contains 13.6 per cent of carbon. Calculate the relative atomic mass of fluorine.**

See Answer 2, p. 62.

This direct method for determining relative atomic masses is limited because carbon does not form many compounds of this type, that is consisting of carbon and *one* other element, but once the relative atomic mass of oxygen and a few other elements has been determined, the method can be extended in various ways. For example, although the element tin does not combine directly with carbon, it does combine with oxygen to form tin dioxide (SnO_2). Once the relative atomic mass of oxygen has been determined, it can be used to determine the relative atomic mass of tin.

> **Tin dioxide contains 78.8 per cent of tin. The relative atomic mass of oxygen is 16. Calculate the relative atomic mass of tin.**

See Answer 3, p. 62.

In this way can be built up an interdependent series of determinations of relative atomic mass by accurate determinations of the percentage composition of pure compounds of known molecular formula. This is the method which was used during the nineteenth and early twentieth centuries. However, there are a number of factors which limit its accuracy. The compounds used for the determinations must have no trace of impurity. This is in itself difficult and rigorous methods of purification must be employed; these however sometimes slightly change the relative proportions of isotopes present in the sample. Furthermore, the method involves manipulative techniques of the highest order if accurate results are to be obtained and the experimental errors accumulate with each succeeding determination in a series.

> **Can you explain why this should be?**

We start our series of determinations with the premise that the relative atomic mass of carbon is exactly 12. Suppose we determine the relative atomic mass of oxygen and there is an error in our determination. The relative atomic mass of oxygen so determined will be incorrect. If we now use this relative atomic mass of oxygen in the determination of the relative atomic mass of tin, any experimental errors in this determination will be accumulated with the original error.

21

However, there is a more fundamental difficulty than these experimental ones. In the determination of the atomic mass of an element there are three factors involved:

1 the percentage composition of the compound under examination;
2 the relative numbers of atoms of the various elements in the compound;
3 the atomic masses of those elements.

Knowledge of any *two* of these factors makes it possible to calculate the third. Normally, however, only the percentage composition of the compound can be determined. Determination of the atomic mass of an element usually then involves making an informed assumption about the relative numbers of atoms in the compound.

The modern physical method for determining relative atomic mass is much more direct: much smaller quantities of material are used; impurities do not effect the result; almost any compound of the element concerned may be used for the determination. By these means a relative atomic mass can be determined with considerable accuracy, under favourable conditions better than $\pm 0.000\,001$. This method involves the use of a *mass spectrometer*.

mass spectrometer

You will remember that in section 6.1.3 we mentioned J. J. Thomson's determination of the ratio e/m for an electron. The method used depended on the fact that a beam of electrons (which as you will remember have a negative charge) moving in a uniform magnetic field has a path which is an arc of a circle. In the mass spectrometer we convert atoms of the element under examination into positively charged *ions** and then determine their e/m ratio by methods similar to those used by Thomson.

ion

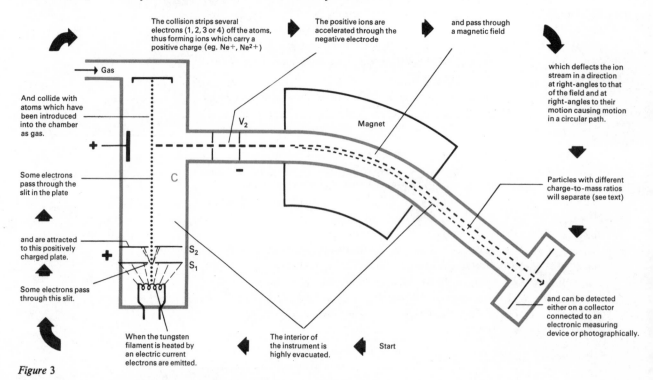

Figure 3

Diagrammatic representation of a mass spectrometer.

---

* An ion *is an atom which has either lost or gained electrons, so becoming either positively or negatively charged. For example, a sodium atom Na on losing an electron (which carries a negative charge) is converted to a positively charged sodium ion Na⁺. Similarly, a chlorine atom Cl on gaining an electron would be converted to a negatively charged ion Cl⁻. Such a negatively charged ion is called a chloride ion, not a chlorine ion, and the names of negative ions usually end in -ide. We will discuss ions in more detail in later parts of this course.*

The essential features of the mass spectrometer are shown in Figure 3.

The whole interior of the apparatus is highly evacuated (10^{-6} Torr).* The tungsten filament is heated by an electric current; this causes it to emit electrons, some of which pass through the slit S_1 and are immediately attracted towards the positively charged plate S_2. Some of these electrons pass through a slit in the plate S_2 and then collide with atoms which have been introduced into the chamber C as vapour. Let us suppose that we introduced neon gas into the chamber. The collision strips off one or two electrons (sometimes three or even four) from the neutral atoms so forming ions which carry one or two (or more) positive charges and which we represent by Ne^+ or Ne^{2+}.

Why do these ions have a *positive* charge? Re-read the last sentence if you are not sure of the answer, remembering that an electron is negatively charged.

These positive ions are then accelerated through the slotted negative electrode, V_2, and then come into a uniform magnetic field. (In Figure 3, imagine that the poles of the magnet are above and below the plane of the paper.) They are deflected by this magnetic field in a direction at right-angles to that of the field and at right-angles to their motion. This makes the ions move in a circular path of such a radius that the magnetic deflecting force (inward) is just equal and opposite to the centrifugal force (outward). The magnetic deflecting force depends on the charge of the ion, on its velocity and on the strength of the magnetic field. The centrifugal force (cf. Unit 3) depends on the mass of the ion, on its velocity and on the radius of curvature of its path. The velocity in turn depends on the accelerating voltage and on the charge on the ion. We can work out an equation relating these quantities (this is done in Appendix 3 (Black) of this Unit); this equation (which you are not required to remember) is:

$$\frac{m}{ne} = \frac{B^2 r^2}{2V}$$

where m is the mass of the ion,

n is the number of positive charges on the ion (which we represented by the $^+$ superscript). (e is, of course, numerically the same as the negative charge on the electron),

B is the magnetic field strength,

r is the radius of the curvature of the ion's path in a magnetic field,

and V is the accelerating voltage.

From this you will see that ions having different values of the charge-to-mass ratio will take different paths as you can see indicated in the diagram. For particles which all have the same positive charge (ne) the path of lighter particles will be more deflected than that of heavier particles.

Which of the ions Ne^+ and Ne^{2+} would you expect to be the more deflected? Why?

The equation shows that if n is increased r must decrease.

After the particles have thus been separated they can be detected either on a collector which is connected with an electronic measuring device, or on a photographic plate which they affect in the same way that light does.

---

* *The torr is the SI unit of pressure (Symbol: Torr). It is named after the Italian scientist Torricelli (1608–47), who developed the mercury barometer to measure the pressure of the atmosphere.* 1 *torr* $= (101\ 325/760)\ N\ m^{-2}$.

In this way, the extent of the deflection of the particles can be measured, and hence their masses relative to one another. If the carbon isotope $^{12}_{6}C$ is chosen as the standard, then this method provides a direct measurement of relative atomic mass.

Moreover, when the element under examination consists of a mixture of isotopes, the mass spectrometer can be used to separate the isotopes and to determine the relative proportions of the isotopes present. By keeping the magnetic field constant and steadily varying the electrical fields the various ions can be brought in turn to focus on the slit. On passing through this they are brought to a stop, giving up their charges to form an electrical current which can be measured by standard methods. A graph, plotting the current strength against the electrical field strength, shows a series of peaks, each peak corresponding to a group of ions having one particular value of ne/m. Such a graph is called a mass spectrum. The magnitude of the current at a given instant is proportional to the number of ions received and so, under controlled conditions, the relative abundance of the ions is proportional to the height of the corresponding peaks on the curve.

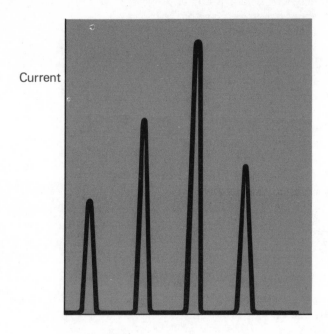

Current

Relative Atomic Mass

Figure 4

A typical mass spectrum.

The presence of four isotopes is shown. The position of each peak is determined by the relative atomic masses of the isotopes concerned, the distance between each peak and the preceding peak corresponding to a difference of approximately 1 a.m.u. in atomic mass. The height of each peak is proportional to the relative amounts of each isotope present.

From this information we can calculate the relative atomic mass of the specimen of the element by simple arithmetic.

> For example, suppose our sample of neon gas in the mass spectrometer consists of three isotopes ^{20}Ne, ^{21}Ne, ^{22}Ne with atomic masses of 19.99, 20.99 and 21.99 and percentage abundance 90.92, 0.257 and 8.82—can you calculate the relative atomic mass of that sample of neon gas?

The method is to multiply each atomic mass by its percentage abundance and divide by 100. The sum of these contributions gives the relative atomic mass. For our neon sample this is 20.18.

6.2.6 Mass defect and binding energy

Precise determinations of relative atomic mass by means of the mass spectrometer have shown that the masses of nuclides are not exactly equal to the sums of the individual masses of their component protons, neutrons and electrons. For example, the atomic mass of $_1^1$H is 1.007825 a.m.u. and the mass of a neutron is 1.008665 a.m.u. The atomic mass of deuterium, $_1^2$H, might therefore be expected to be 2.016490 a.m.u. However, direct determination shows that the atomic mass of deuterium is, in fact, 2.01410 a.m.u. The difference between these two masses, 0.00239 a.m.u. is the *mass defect*, which is defined as the difference between the mass of a nucleus and the sum of the masses of its constituent nucleons.

mass defect

This loss of mass arises from the relationship between mass and energy (cf. Unit 4) and represents the binding energy which holds the nucleus together in the nucleus.

Why do we say that this mass defect represents the binding energy which holds the nucleons together in the nucleus?

As you will see later (Unit 31) the binding energy of the deuterium nucleus is about ten million times the energy liberated in a typical chemical reaction; chemical reactions, as we have already mentioned, do not involve the nucleus but only the electrons.

Suppose we were to pull the nucleus of a deuterium atom apart to form a separated proton and neutron. We would need to find 0.00239 a.m.u. from somewhere in order that the proton and neutron should have their correct masses. We have provided this mass in the form of energy, the energy we have had to put into the system in order to pull the nucleus apart—we have had to do work against the force that binds the nucleons together. The amount of that force or energy—the binding energy—is the mass defect (in kg) multiplied by c^2 where c is the velocity of light 3×10^8 m sec^{-1}.

6.3 Radioactivity

6.3.1 The nature of radioactivity

In some nuclides the nucleus may be unstable and disintegrate spontaneously, the disintegrations being accompanied by the emission of radiations. This is a convenient term to describe a variety of emissions, some of which are streams of particles in the conventional sense, others electromagnetic waves more like radiation in the ordinary sense. Such radiations were first detected by the French physicist Becquerel in 1896 when he noticed that certain salts of uranium could produce a latent image on a photographic plate which could be developed in the same way as the latent image produced by visible light. The radiations from the salts that produced this latent image could penetrate paper and thin sheets of metal. They could also discharge a charged electroscope.

Nuclides which contain such unstable nuclei are said to be *radioactive*. Several types of radiation may be emitted, depending on the nuclide under examination. The best known of these are:

radioactivity

(i) *alpha* (α) *particles*, which are helium atoms which have lost both of their two electrons to form $^4_2He^{2+}$ ions (the loss of two negatively charged electrons leaves an ion carrying a double positive charge). These bare helium nuclei consist of two protons and two neutrons bound together particularly strongly.

alpha particle

(ii) *beta* (β) *particles* which are electrons which may be travelling at extremely high velocities approaching that of light (3×10^8 ms^{-1}). These electrons arise because the neutron itself is unstable and will change into a proton and an electron with the release of energy. When a neutron in a nucleus undergoes this transformation the resulting electron is promptly emitted as a β-particle.

beta particle

(iii) *gamma* (γ) *radiation* which is an electromagnetic radiation of very short wavelengths, usually very much shorter even than those of X-rays.*

gamma radiation

These radiations will be demonstrated in the television programme of Unit 31.

6.3.2 Half-life

The rate at which a radioactive nuclide emits particles is unaffected by the chemical or physical state of the sample. For example, the rate at which uranium emits α-particles is the same whether the uranium is existing as a free metal or is combined with other atoms; it is the same at red-heat as it is at room temperature.

The rate at which a radioactive sample emits particles is dependent only on the kind and number of nuclei present. Since for any particular nuclide sample the rate is proportional to the number of nuclei, it follows that

---

* *Other 'rays' which are less frequently met include neutrons (which carry no charge, have mass of about 1 a.m.u. and may be symbolized ^1_0n); protons $^1_1H^+$; deuterons $^2_1H^+$; positrons (which may be regarded as particles with the mass of an electron and unit positive charge) symbolized either as e^+ or β^+; there are also neutrinos which are particles with zero rest mass and zero charge.*

the rate is continuously decreasing because the number of nuclei left is continuously being reduced. If the sample initially contains a certain number (x) of nuclei, then after the period of time called the *half-life*, only one half $\left(\dfrac{x}{2}\right)$ of the original number of nuclei will be left and the rate of decay at that time will be half what it was initially.

You were introduced to this type of behaviour in Unit 2 and in particular learned the meaning of the term half-life. If you do not remember this clearly read Unit 2. section 2.5.4 again.

6.3.3 Half-life periods of some nuclides

Half-life periods vary considerably from nuclide to nuclide, from 10^{-21} seconds to 10^{10} years. The table in the margin shows the half-life periods of some nuclides (do not attempt to remember these). Stable isotopes are given in brackets.

The principle of the use of naturally-occurring radioactive nuclides, especially $^{40}_{19}K$, $^{87}_{37}Rb$ and $^{235}_{92}U$, in determining the age of rock samples in which they are found, has been discussed in Unit 2.

The *specific activity*, S, of a nuclide is defined as the number of disintegrations per unit of mass in unit time. This is usually expressed in curie per g, where one curie is 3.70×10^{10} disintegrations per second.

specific activity

The specific activity of a radioactive material can be measured with a Geiger counter.* This is done by comparing the number of impulses (counts) produced per minute in a Geiger counter with the number produced by a standard sample under the same conditions.

6.3.4 The effects of radioactive disintegration

When an α-particle ($^{4}_{2}He^{2+}$ or $^{4}_{2}\alpha$) is emitted by a nucleus, that nucleus loses two protons and two neutrons.

What effect would this have on (i) the atomic number, and (ii) the mass number?

The loss of two protons means that the atomic number is reduced by two, that is the original element is converted into a different element whose atomic number is two units less. The mass number is reduced by four.

In the emission of an α-particle from the $^{238}_{92}U$ nucleus what would be the atomic number of the element formed? What would its mass number be?

* *A counter is a device which detects and measures ionizing radiations. The best known of these is the Geiger-Müller counter (usually referred to as a Geiger counter) the operation of which depends on the fact that when the radiation passes into a gas the gas is ionized and will conduct a current. In the Geiger counter this current is amplified and may be recorded as such or converted to an audible signal, so making it possible to measure the intensity of the radiation.*

Nuclide	Half-life
$^{3}_{1}H$	12.26 years
$^{6}_{4}Be$	4×10^{-21} seconds
$^{7}_{4}Be$	53 days
$^{8}_{4}Be$	3×10^{-16} seconds
($^{9}_{4}Be$	stable)
$^{10}_{4}Be$	2.7×10^{6} years
$^{11}_{4}Be$	13.6 seconds
$^{10}_{6}C$	19 seconds
$^{11}_{6}C$	20.5 minutes
($^{12}_{6}C$	stable)
($^{13}_{6}C$	stable)
$^{14}_{6}C$	5770 years*
$^{15}_{6}C$	2.25 seconds
$^{16}_{6}C$	0.74 seconds
$^{18}_{9}F$	1.87 hours
($^{19}_{9}F$	stable)
$^{22}_{11}Na$	2.58 years
($^{23}_{11}Na$	stable)
$^{32}_{15}P$	14.3 days
($^{32}_{16}S$	stable)
$^{35}_{16}S$	87 days
$^{40}_{19}K$	1.3×10^{9} years*
($^{40}_{20}Ca$	stable)
$^{87}_{37}Rb$	4.7×10^{10} years*
$^{90}_{38}Sr$	28 years
$^{137}_{55}Cs$	30 years
$^{235}_{92}U$	7.13×10^{8} years*
$^{238}_{92}U$	4.51×10^{9} years

* *Occurs naturally.*

27

We can write an equation for this type of reaction.*

$$^{238}_{92}\text{U} \rightarrow ^{4}_{2}\alpha + ^{234}_{90}\text{Th}$$

You will see that the loss of two protons changes a uranium atom to a thorium atom and that the loss of four in the mass number is shown in the superscript numbers.

What would be the product when $^{230}_{90}\text{Th}$ emits an α-particle?

See Answer 4, p. 62.

Emission of a β-particle is the emission of unit negative charge from the nucleus.

What would you expect to be the result of this?

The mass number will therefore remain the same but the (positive) nuclear charge will increase by one unit, that is the atomic number would

increase or decrease?

Increase by one unit. For example, when an atom of $^{14}_{6}\text{C}$ emits a β-particle, it forms an atom of

Which element? Which isotope?

Nitrogen, isotope 14, i.e. $^{14}_{7}\text{N}$, by the process

$$^{14}_{6}\text{C} \xrightarrow{\quad \beta^- \quad} ^{14}_{7}\text{N}$$

What nuclide is produced by a β-emission from the nucleus of $^{87}_{36}\text{Kr}$?

See Answer 5, p. 62.

6.3.5 The transmutation of nuclides in the laboratory

Bombardment of a nucleus with high energy particles will sometimes effect the transformation of one nuclide to another. This is the basis of the methods used to make unstable nuclides in the laboratory and will be discussed further in Unit 31.

---

* *In these reactions the α-particle is emitted with considerable kinetic energy and the emission of a β-particle with the emission of a neutrino. These effects do not alter the equations relating to the nuclear changes. Such reactions will be discussed more fully in Unit 31.*

6.4 Spectra

6.4.1 The electrons

Here we will leave the nucleus for the time being. You will find a fuller discussion of it in Unit 31.

We mentioned earlier that the chemical properties of substances are determined by the electrons surrounding the nucleus rather than by the nucleus itself. We are now going to try to build up a picture of the arrangements of the electrons in atoms. We will be using information (obtained from atomic spectra) on the energies required to produce certain changes in the arrangements of the electrons in atoms. We will try to establish regularities in the electronic arrangements of atoms of different elements and then link these to the chemical properties of the elements. In the process of building a picture of the electronic structure of atoms we will also lay the foundations for a discussion of the ways in which atoms combine to make molecules (which you will meet in later Units).

We have previously said that

(a) in a neutral atom, the number of electrons must be the same as the number of protons in the nucleus; that is, the same as the atomic number;

(b) the electrons can be removed. This results in a deficiency of negative charge and leaves behind positively charged ions.

We are now going to look more closely at the arrangements of these electrons and see how they lead to the different chemical properties of the elements.

It was explained in Unit 2 that one cannot hope to see electrons by using electromagnetic radiation. (If you do not remember the arguments from Unit 2, have another look at them—they are associated with the wavelength of the radiation used and the size of the object being viewed.) However, very useful information about the *arrangements* of the electrons can be obtained by studying electromagnetic radiation. First we need to examine electromagnetic radiation a little more closely (it will be treated in more detail in Unit 28).

6.4.2 Dispersion of light

In Unit 2 you had the equation connecting the wavelength, frequency and velocity of a wave motion. Here it is again:

$$v = f\lambda$$

where v is the velocity of the wave motion which we could measure in metres per second ($m\ s^{-1}$).
f is the frequency which we measure in hertz (Hz) (cf. Unit 2).
λ is the wavelength. If we use the units for f and λ above, the wavelengths must be expressed in metres (for the procedure used by spectroscopists see Appendix 4 (Black), p. 51).

If you are dealing with electromagnetic radiation, v represents the velocity of light: it is normal to use the symbol c for this, particularly when referring to electromagnetic radiation in a vacuum. Thus the equation becomes

$$c = f\lambda$$

The wavelengths of visible light lie between 4 and 7×10^{-7} m, but will often be expressed in ångström, e.g. 4 000 ångström.
where c (vacuum) is very nearly 3×10^8 m s^{-1}.

What is the frequency of light with $\lambda = 4\,000$ ångström?

If you did not get $f = 7.5 \times 10^{14}$ Hz examine the working given.

$$4\,000\,\text{\AA} = 4\,000 \times 10^{-10}\text{ m}$$
$$= 4 \times 10^3 \times 10^{-10}\text{ m}$$
$$= 4 \times 10^{-7}\text{ m}.$$

$$c = f\lambda \text{ so } f = \frac{c}{\lambda}$$
$$= \frac{3 \times 10^8}{4 \times 10^{-7}}$$
$$= 0.75 \times 10^{15}$$

$$f = 7.5 \times 10^{14}\text{ Hz}$$

This equation normally refers to the velocity of light in a vacuum. In Unit 2, you learnt that the velocity of light is different in different transparent media, though in air it is much the same as in a vacuum. The change in velocity from one transparent medium to another results in the phenomenon of refraction, that is, the light bends from its path. For example:

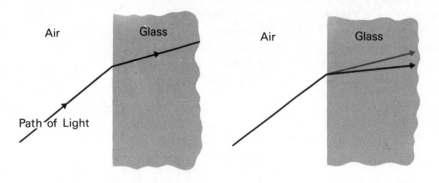

Figure 5

Refraction of light.

Figure 6

Dispersion of light.

The amount of bending at a given surface is dependent on wavelength, so that if there are several wavelengths of light present each will be bent through a different angle.

This phenomenon is known as *dispersion of light*. Note that, while the velocity and wavelength are different in different media, the frequency does not change and is a fundamental property of the electromagnetic radiation. In other words we are saying that v_{glass} is less than c, $(v_\text{g} < c)$ and $\lambda_\text{g} < \lambda_0$ (where λ_0 is the wavelength in a vacuum), whereas f remains constant.

dispersion of light

If you wanted to view the effects of this dispersion you would have to get inside the second transparent medium (glass in the above case!). A simpler alternative is to let the light come out into the first medium again. If this is done using a parallel-sided block (of glass say), the dispersion and bending effects are reversed and the light then travels parallel to its previous path (as explained in Unit 2). The wavelengths (colours in visible light) which were separated out on entry by dispersion at the surface are then recombined and the light follows a path parallel to the original ray, as shown in Unit 2.

6.4.3 The spectrum

To view dispersion of light, a prism of the denser material is used. When the light leaves the prism it is still dispersed.

The resulting light is visibly separated according to wavelength and so shows an electromagnetic spectrum.

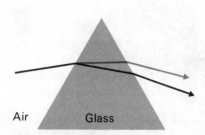

Figure 7

Dispersion of light in a prism.

continuous spectrum

solar spectrum

Light dispersed in this way is also separated in terms of energy. You probably know this already. For example, you will be aware that ultra-violet radiation (wavelengths shorter than visible light) causes sunburn whereas infra-red radiation (wavelengths longer than red light) only warms you.

Blue.

As you saw in Unit 2 electromagnetic radiation from an atom is emitted in discrete amounts. These can be regarded as 'packets' of energy. What is true about electromagnetic radiation emitted from atoms is true of all electromagnetic radiation. These 'packets' of energy are called *photons*. The energy of a photon depends upon the frequency of the light involved. From your answer above, for example, the photons of blue light have larger energies than those of red light. The relationship between the frequency of the radiation and the energy of the photons is

photon

$$E = hf$$

where E = energy of photons measured in joule (cf. Unit 4)

f = frequency of radiation (Hz)

h = a constant called *Planck's constant*, with value 6.626×10^{-34} joule seconds.

Planck's constant

The relation between wavelength and the energy of the photon is then given by combining two of the equations above as follows:

$$E = hf$$
$$c = f\lambda$$

So $$E = \frac{hc}{\lambda}$$

The energy of the photons is less at longer wavelengths.

6.4.4 Atomic spectra

In all these spectra you will have seen distinct bright lines. In the flame spectrum, a bright yellow line is the most prominent feature against the background of the normal continuous flame spectrum. For the sodium street light you would only see a series of lines including this same bright yellow one. In the spectrum of a fluorescent tube you would see bright lines against a continuous spectrum background. These bright lines are *atomic spectra* and have resulted from atoms that have been heated, in the flame or otherwise, giving out light. The atoms gain energy from the flame and some of this energy goes into transferring the electrons into a higher energy state and they are then later able to give energy out again. We see this emitted energy in the form of light of a characteristic wavelength. You will recall that two such characteristic wavelengths are used to establish the standards of length and time (see Unit 2).

atomic spectra

> **Experiment**
>
> **Using the same procedure view the flame spectra from the five samples supplied. Record your results as before.**

You will notice that all these spectra consist of sharp bright lines. Each of the lines is an image, at one particular wavelength, of the slit of the spectroscope. The spectra are called *line spectra* and, as you no doubt observed, they are all different. In fact, each atom has a specific individual atomic spectrum. The element helium was first 'discovered' by detecting an unknown atomic spectrum in the solar spectrum; it was more than 20 years later (in 1895) that the gas was discovered on Earth.

line spectra

One use of atomic spectra is in analytical identification of elements. As each spectrum is specific to one particular element, the elements in a mixture can be identified from the spectrum of the mixture. This is an exceedingly sensitive test as it requires only a very small amount of material to obtain a spectrum.

> **Experiment**
>
> **Examine the spectrum of a mixture of lithium and calcium salts and compare the results with the individual spectra that you have already recorded. Examine the unknown substance and indicate which metals you think are present in the sample by marking the appropriate spaces on your CMA sheet. (See CMA S100 45.)**

On the cover of this Unit there are photographs of the visible parts of the spectra for hydrogen, neon, sodium, mercury and iron, as well as a continuous spectrum from a tungsten filament lamp.

6.4.5 Emission spectra

The atomic spectra which appear as bright lines (you have viewed them in your spectroscope) are called *emission spectra*.

emission spectra

As we have said above, when atoms are heated in a flame their electrons gain some energy from it. The electrons then return to their former state, giving out the absorbed energy again in the form of photons of radiation which appear as the emission spectrum. If light consisting of a continuous spectrum is shone through an atomic vapour, in suitable circumstances, the emergent spectrum is no longer continuous but contains dark lines indicating that some of the original radiation is missing. What has happened is that electrons in the atoms have interacted with radiation of particular wavelengths and absorbed some of it. These dark lines on a continuous spectrum background make up what is called an *absorption spectrum*. This effect will be demonstrated in the TV programme associated with Unit 7.

6.4.6 Absorption spectra

In absorption spectra, photons from the light coming to the sample are absorbed and the electrons gain energy (in general moving further from the nucleus). In emission spectra the electrons are losing energy (in general moving closer to the nucleus) and this energy appears as photons.

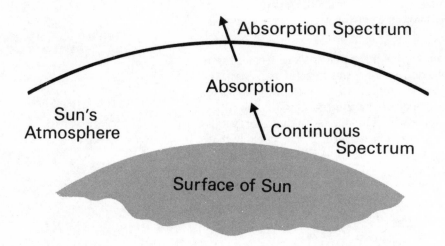

Figure 8

Absorption of light by the Sun's atmosphere.

More accurately, for absorption the electrons absorb specific photons but, as with the energy gained from the flame, in the vast majority of atoms the electron then returns to its former position and regains its former energy. In doing this the electron emits a photon of the same energy that was absorbed. These photons, however, are emitted in random directions and so are missing from the spectrum that is observed.

> **If you get a fairly good clear day look carefully at the solar spectrum (you can sometimes increase the intensity of the light by reflecting the sunlight off a shiny spoon).**
>
> **DO NOT POINT YOUR SPECTROSCOPE IN THE DIRECTION OF THE SUN.**
>
> **The dark lines you will see are called Fraunhofer lines, after their discoverer, and are caused by the light from the Sun's surface passing through the atomic atmosphere of the Sun, where certain photons are absorbed. This absorption spectrum tells us something about the composition of the Sun's atmosphere.**

6.5 Energy Levels

6.5.1 Electron 'jumps'

What information can the spectra give us about the electrons, and their arrangement in the atoms?

You know from previous work that the (negative) electron will be attracted towards the (positive) nucleus by a force given by Coulomb's Law.

If an electron is to be moved from a given point to a new one further from the nucleus, work will have to be done against this force of attraction. In other words, energy will have to be supplied to the electron (you have done this using the energy in a flame). If the electron now returns to its former position, the attractive force will assist the move and energy will be released by the electron (the energy released will be the same as that added in the first move, as required by the Law of Conservation of Energy). The energy so released appears as photons of electromagnetic radiation. These considerations explain why we said above that the electron is changing energy when it interacts with radiation and also why we implied that the energy change is associated with a change in position. Both of these changes suggest as an analogy a picture of the electron 'jumping', the 'jumps' being both 'energy jumps' and 'position jumps'.

You will notice that what we are doing is finding out about the behaviour of electrons by experiment (spectra in this case). We will interpret the evidence we obtain by seeking analogies from our experience of the behaviour of particles, waves, fluids, fogs, etc. (see Unit 30 as well as this and the next Unit). For the time being, terms like 'position' and 'arrangement' will be used but should not be thought to imply that these refer to static pictures of particles, etc.

Let us now return to a consideration of atomic spectra. Spectra give direct evidence about electron energy 'jumps' (we will return to the question of position a little later).

To start with take the spectrum of the simplest atom, the hydrogen atom, which has only one electron. The spectrum consists of a series of sharp lines. (See the cover of this Unit.)

What does this suggest to you about the energy changes that the electrons undergo in giving out the photons for this spectrum?
Problem: Calculate the energy of the photons emitted in the red line of the hydrogen spectrum by using the calibration under the spectrum and the equation $E = hf$ given above.

Each of the lines in the spectrum is caused by an electron 'jumping' from one energy level to another (lower energy) one, and at the same time emitting a photon whose energy corresponds to the energy difference

Two conclusions might have suggested themselves to you:

(1) the possible energy 'jumps' are limited;
(2) the energy 'jumps' are very specific in size.

Problem:
$E = 3.0 \times 10^{-19}$ J.

between the two levels. Here are the energy values for the photons emitted in four of the lines of the hydrogen spectrum. (If you did not get the correct answer to the last problem, examine the working for the blue line of the hydrogen spectrum that is given below the table).

Table 1   *Energy values (hydrogen spectrum)*

Line	red	light blue	1st violet	2nd violet
f (Hz)	4.568×10^{14}	6.167×10^{14}	6.907×10^{14}	7.309×10^{14}
E (Joule)	3.027×10^{-19}	4.086×10^{-19}	4.577×10^{-19}	4.843×10^{-19}

$$E = hf$$
$$h = 6.626 \times 10^{-34} \text{ joule sec}$$
$$f = 6.167 \times 10^{14} \text{ Hz from spectrum}$$
$$E = 6.626 \times 10^{-34} \times 6.167 \times 10^{14}$$
$$= 4.086 \times 10^{-19} \text{ joule}$$

6.5.2   Energy-level diagram

Only the visible part of the hydrogen spectrum is shown on the cover plate. The lines in this part of the spectrum are called the Balmer series (of lines), after the man who first discovered a simple mathematical relationship between their wavelengths. This relationship, which we do not propose to discuss here (but see Appendix 5 (Black) if you are interested), establishes that each of the 'jumps' producing the Balmer lines are made to one particular energy level. This enables us to calculate the energies of all the other levels relative to this lowest one. By taking this level as a base and measuring each of the jumps from it, the position of the various energy levels can be shown diagrammatically.

Figure 9

Energy levels for the hydrogen atom (Exercise, p. 37).

Exercise

On Figure 9 draw (horizontal) lines to represent the energy levels for the hydrogen atom that are involved in the spectral lines listed in Table 1. From the table you can see that the largest jump involved for these four lines is 4.843×10^{-19} joule. A suitable scale is 1 cm $= 1 \times 10^{-19}$ joule. Draw a line 18 cm above the bottom of your page (the reason for this will become clear later). This line will represent the energy level to which the electrons are jumping. This represents the lowest energy level involved in the Balmer Series. It is then a matter of placing another line at a position corresponding to 3.027×10^{-19} joule above this line. The third line will be at a position corresponding to 4.086×10^{-19} joule above the lowest energy level. When you have completed the diagram in this way with five lines (the lowest, plus the four 'jumps'), what you have is an *energy-level diagram* for the electron energy levels in a hydrogen atom.

The Balmer lines are the result of the electron jumping from the upper energy levels on your diagram to the lowest level you have drawn. Jumps could be represented by arrows as shown in the answer diagram, where the arrows represent jumps from higher to lower levels and hence the emission of photons, leading to the emission spectrum. To represent the jumps that take place on absorption of photons (resulting in an absorption spectrum) the arrows would go in the opposite direction.

There is in fact an energy level below the lowest level that gives rise to the Balmer lines. This level is lower by 16.34×10^{-19} joule and is the lowest energy level in the hydrogen atom. It is called the *ground state* energy level, and when the electron is in it the atom is said to be in its ground state. The electron will then be closer to the nucleus than in any other energy level. If the ground state level is added to the energy-level diagram, it will now look like Figure 11.

All levels except the ground state energy level are called *excited states*.

6.5.3 The Lyman series

A series of jumps is clearly possible, each finishing in the ground state level. Each of these jumps would result in the emission of a photon, giving another series of spectral lines.

Exercise

Put the ground state energy level into your energy-level diagram and indicate the jumps down to this level by arrows.

Calculate the energy changes for the lowest four of these 'jumps' and from these energy jumps (ΔE) calculate the frequencies of the spectral lines that would result. Put the values you get in Table 2 and show what the spectrum would look like by drawing lines on the calibrated blank below the table.

Table 2

Line	1st	2nd	3rd	4th
ΔE (J)				
f (Hz)				

2.0 x 10^{15} Hz   3.0 x 10^{15} Hz

This series of lines is called the *Lyman series* and occurs in the ultra-violet region of the electromagnetic spectrum.

energy-level diagram

Your diagram should look like this, without the arrows.

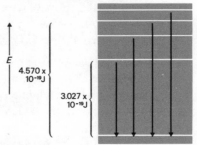

Figure 10

Energy levels for the Balmer series.

ground state

excited state

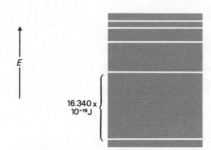

Figure 11

Energy levels for the hydrogen atom.

The answer is in the next margin overleaf.

37

You will no doubt have noticed that the lines of both the Balmer series and the Lyman series get closer together as you go to higher frequencies in the spectrum, that is to shorter wavelengths.

Summary

At this stage it is worth considering what we have so far established about the electron in the hydrogen atom. From examining the lines in the atomic spectrum you can

(a) see that only a very few discrete energy changes are possible;
(b) measure these changes.

The easiest explanation of these phenomena is the one that we have assumed without stating it (had you noticed?), that is, that only specific energy levels are possible.

From the sizes of the energy jumps observed, you can calculate the relative energies of these levels and you have shown this on your energy-level diagram (as other atomic spectra also consists of lines you might expect to be able to do the same for them).

At this stage you should have numerous questions in your mind. Before you read further try listing some of these questions.

Some of the questions you might have asked are:

(a) Why are only specific energy levels possible?
(b) Do specific energy levels imply that only a few specific distances of separation between the electron and the nucleus are possible?
   (If Coulomb's Law applies, it would certainly appear so.)
(c) We have only talked about energy levels relative to each other; can we relate them to anything else?
(d) How does the electron 'jump'?

Many other questions might have occurred to you and many would be related to those listed above.

At this stage we do not propose to attempt to answer (a), and hence (b). An explanation in terms of the behaviour of an electron will be given in Unit 30. Until then, you will have to accept that this is the best interpretation of the atomic spectra. Some of the questions that occur to you, (d) for example, you will later find cannot be answered in a simple manner.

6.5.4   The relation between energy levels

What we hope to do now is show that we can get more information from the energy levels.

First examine the information we have about these levels. We said that there is a mathematical relationship between the lines of the Balmer series, so there should be a mathematical relationship between the energy levels in the hydrogen atom. Without going into this in detail we can illustrate it graphically.

Exercise

Number the levels on your energy-level diagram, starting, for convenience, with 1 for the ground state. On Figure 13, plot energy (E) against the number of the level (n).

The scale is 1 cm $=1 \times 10^{-19}$ J for E and 2 cm $=1$ unit for n.

The first two points are shown ($n=1$, $E=0$ and $n=2$, $E=16.34 \times 10^{-19}$ J).

Complete the graph from the values in Table 3.

By extending your graph beyond $n=6$, determine a value for the energy of the seventh level ($n=7$). This procedure is called extrapolating your graph.

Here are the values of the frequencies of the Lyman series that you have just calculated and a diagrammatic representation of the spectrum. If your answers were incorrect examine the calculation given and compare this with your own calculation.

Table 3

ΔE (J)	f (Hz)
16.340×10^{-19}	2.466×10^{15}
19.367×10^{-19}	2.923×10^{15}
20.426×10^{-19}	3.083×10^{15}
20.917×10^{-19}	3.157×10^{15}
21.183×10^{-19}	

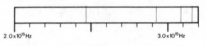

2.0×10^{15} Hz 3.0×10^{15} Hz

Figure 12

$\Delta E = 16.340 \times 10^{-19}$ joule

$\Delta E = hf$

$f = \dfrac{\Delta E}{h} = \dfrac{16.340 \times 10^{-19}}{6.626 \times 10^{-34}}$

$\quad = 2.466 \times 10^{15}$ Hz

The limiting value of E is 21.74×10^{-19} J. You should have obtained a value within 0.1×10^{-19} J of this.

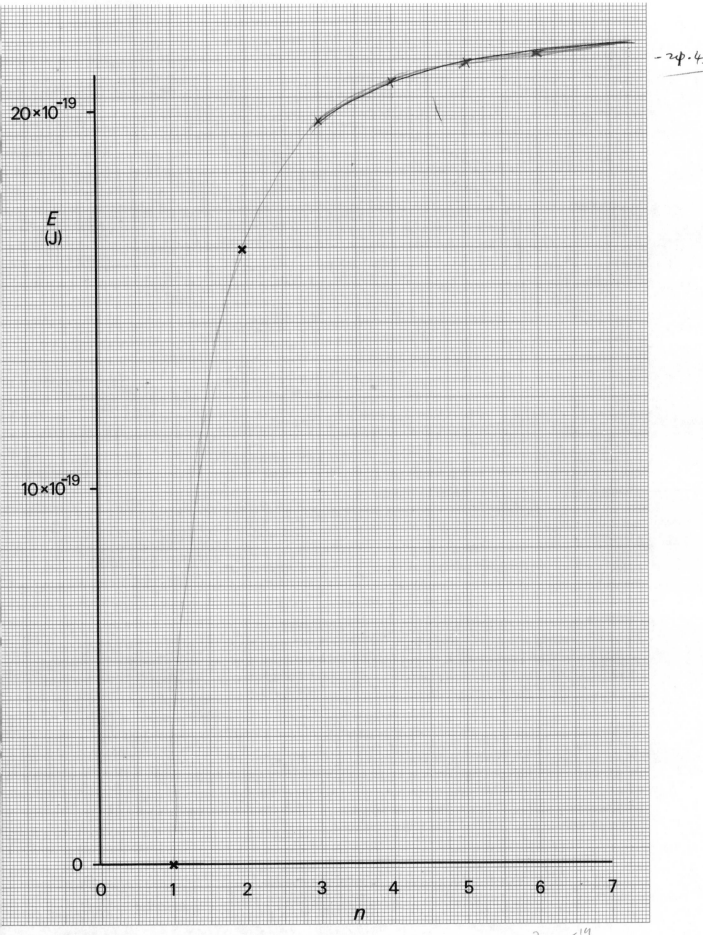

20×10⁻¹⁹ —

10×10⁻¹⁹ —

E
(J)

0

0   1   2   3   4   5   6   7

n

-2φ.4.

21.47 ? ×10⁻¹⁹

Figure 13

Determination of the energy of the n=7 *level in hydrogen. (Exercise, p. 38)*

The energy you have just read from your extrapolated graph is of course the size of the energy involved in an electron 'jump' from the seventh level of the hydrogen atom to the first (ground state) level and hence is the energy of the next line of the Lyman series. Your graph should look like Figure 14.

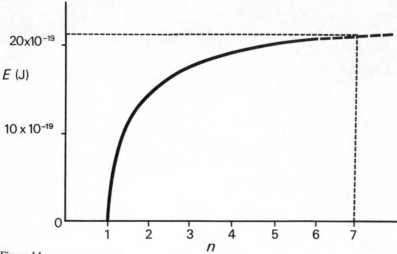

Figure 14

Relationship between energy (E) *and number of the energy level* (n).

The actual value for $n=7$ is $E= 21.36 \times 10^{-19}$ joule. It is of course difficult to obtain this value accurately from an extrapolation of a curved graph.

As you will already have observed, it is clear that, as the energy levels become higher, the consecutive energy levels are closer together. As the electron can have only the energies indicated on the energy-level diagram, the procedure you have just used of numbering these is a useful shorthand way of referring to them. For example, the $n=2$ level means the level where $E=16.340 \times 10^{-19}$ joule above the ground state level.

6.5.5 Quantum numbers

This numbering procedure is a general one. If you had the mathematical relationship for your graph, you could obtain the value of E for any particular energy level, i.e. for any value of n, from your graph, or by substituting in the mathematical equation connecting E and n.

The only possible values of n are the numbers 1, 2, 3, 4, etc. and these numbers are called *quantum numbers*. The actual numbers (n) you have used are called the *principal quantum numbers* for the electronic energies of the hydrogen atom, and using the letter n is the normal way of denoting this number.

quantum number

principal quantum number

Return now to your graph. It is clear from this that it will not be necessary for n to get much greater than 6 before you would be unable to obtain different values of E for consecutive values of n from your graph. $n=9$ and $n=10$ would probably give you almost the same value of E. In other words, no matter how high n gets, E will have a limiting value and that will be less than 22×10^{-19} joules. You could determine the limiting value for n from your graph if you had a few more values of E (for $n=7$, 8, etc.) or if you knew the mathematical relationship between E and n.

Another way of finding this same limiting value of E would be to try and find the value of E when the difference between successive energy levels became indistinguishable from 0; the difference between successive energy levels, of course, being the value of E for $n=3$ less the value of E for $n=2$, say, which we could write $E_{n=3}-E_{n=2}$ or, more simply, just E_3-E_2 where E_3 stands for the energy of the energy level where $n=3$. For the general case, we would write this as $E_{n+1}-E_n$.

Exercise

Complete Table 4 which shows the energy difference between one energy level and the succeeding one. Complete the graph on Figure 15, which is a plot of $E_{n+1} - E_n$ against E_n. Extrapolate the graph to $E_{n+1} - E_n = 0$ and hence determine the limiting value of E_n. The scale of the graph is 2 cm $= 1 \times 10^{-19}$ J for E and 4 cm $= 1 \times 10^{-19}$ J for $E_{n+1} - E_n$.

Table 4

E_2	E_3	E_4
16.340×10^{-19}	19.367×10^{-19}	20.426×10^{-19}
E_5	E_6	E_7
20.917×10^{-19}	21.183×10^{-19}	21.36×10^{-19}

E_3-E_2	E_4-E_3	E_5-E_4
3.027×10^{-19}	1.059×10^{-19}	0.491×10^{-9}
E_6-E_5	E_7-E_6	
0.266×10^{-19}	0.18×10^{-19}	

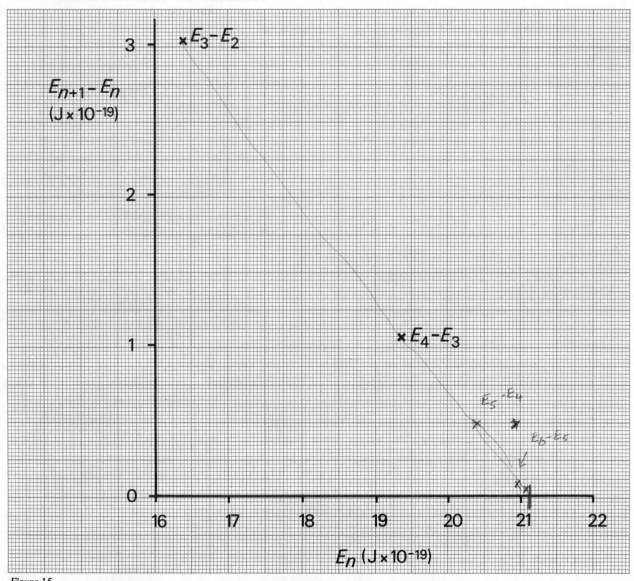

Figure 15

Relationship between energy differences ($\triangle$E) and energy (E). (Exercise, p. 41)

What is the significance of this limiting value of E (we write this E, n large, or E_∞)? Consider an atom in its ground state, that is with its electron with principal quantum number $n=1$. If this atom interacts with a photon of energy 16.340×10^{-19} joule the electron will absorb the photon and 'jump' to the level with the principal quantum number 2. Similarly if the ground state hydrogen atom absorbs a photon of 20.426×10^{-19} joule will jump to the level with the principal quantum number 4 (and this could be observed as an absorption line in the Lyman series).

> **What will happen if the ground state atom absorbs a photon with energy of 21.8×10^{-19} joule?**

This is just greater than the limiting value of the energy levels of the hydrogen atom. The electron would no longer be in an energy level of the atom. It would fly away from the nucleus completely.

6.5.6 Ionization energy

The minimum energy to remove or ionize an electron in its ground state is the same as the limiting energy of the energy levels E_∞, and is called the *ionization energy*. In the above example you determined the value of the ionization energy for hydrogen.

ionization energy

> **Think back a moment. Can the ground state hydrogen atom absorb a photon of energy 17.0×10^{-19} joule?**

No, there is no energy 'jump' corresponding to 17.0×10^{-19} joule, so the electron cannot absorb this photon.

> **Can a ground state hydrogen atom absorb a photon of 22.0×10^{-19} joule?**

Yes, in this case 21.74×10^{19} joule goes into ionizing the electron and the excess energy will then appear as kinetic energy of the electron and nucleus moving in opposite directions.

6.5.7 The complete hydrogen spectrum

We have discussed the Balmer and Lyman series in the hydrogen spectrum. Other series of lines also exist. For example, electron jumps from levels with $n>3$ to the $n=3$ level result in the Paschen series which is found in the infra-red region of the electromagnetic spectrum.

The relative positions of the various series of spectral lines in the hydrogen atomic spectrum are shown in Figure 16.

> **Take your energy-level diagram and draw on it all the 'jumps' that you have calculated for the Balmer series and the lowest three for the Paschen series.**

You will notice that there are very few possible energy 'jumps' that you have not filled in on your energy-level diagram. For example, you should not have arrows connecting $n=5$ and $n=4$. This 'jump' as well as the other possible jumps make up parts of other series of lines that you have not dealt with.

On your energy-level diagram you have the energy differences between the levels. Also you know that the ground state energy is the lowest energy the electron can have. We have called the ground state energy $E=0$ (that is, $E=0$ for the $n=1$ level).

Each energy level has its own value of E (for example, for $n=2$ $E=16.340 \times 10^{-19}$ J).

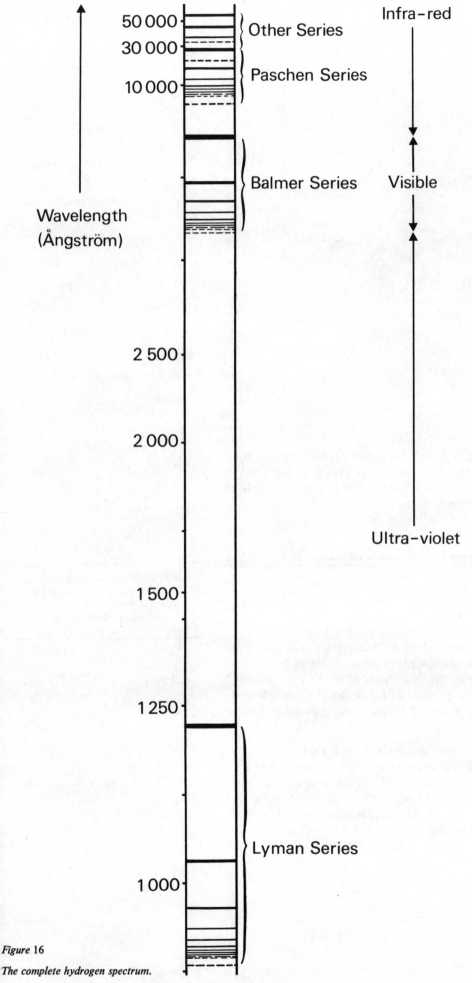

Figure 16

The complete hydrogen spectrum.

The ionization energy is the limiting energy of the energy levels in the atom. Figure 17 is then the energy-level diagram for the hydrogen atom.

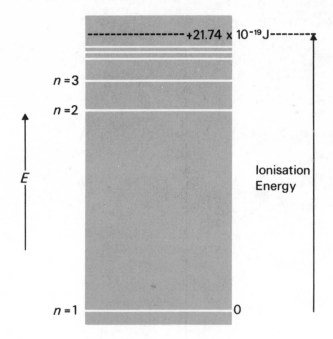

Figure 17

Energy-level diagram for hydrogen.

Now that you have determined the limiting energy-level value (E_∞) you can easily calculate the minimum energy required to remove an electron from any particular energy level. From $n=1$ it is the ionization energy 21.74×10^{-19} joule. For the $n=2$ level it will be 16.340×10^{-19} joule less than this, that is 5.40×10^{-19} joule.

Would you expect the ionization energy for different atoms to be the same?

No, each nucleus has a different charge so that one would expect that an electron in the ground state energy level would require differing amounts of energy to remove it from its nucleus.

We have dealt at length with the hydrogen spectrum and the hydrogen atom. From the spectrum we introduced the idea of energy levels and quantum numbers. By measuring the frequencies of the spectral lines we have determined the possible energy levels of the electron in the hydrogen atom and by extrapolating these have determined the ionization energy for hydrogen.

We have treated hydrogen at length because it is the easiest spectrum to interpret. The ideas we have introduced are applicable to other atoms but the interpretation of a spectrum is more difficult when more than one electron is involved. The next Unit will deal with the electronic structure of many-electron atoms and extend the concepts that we have introduced here. The electronic structures we will arrive at in Unit 7 will help you to understand the chemistry of the various elements. The link to the chemistry will occur in Unit 8.

Appendix 1

Table of Elements

(a) In order of atomic number

Atomic number	Element	Symbol	Relative atomic mass	Atomic number	Element	Symbol	Relative atomic mass
1	Hydrogen	H	1.008	53	Iodine	I	126.9045
2	Helium	He	4.00260	54	Xenon	Xe	131.30
3	Lithium	Li	6.941	55	Cesium	Cs	132.9055
4	Beryllium	Be	9.01218	56	Barium	Ba	137.34
5	Boron	B	10.81	57	Lanthanum	La	138.9055
6	Carbon	C	12.011	58	Cerium	Ce	140.12
7	Nitrogen	N	14.0067	59	Praseodymium	Pr	140.0977
8	Oxygen	O	15.9994	60	Neodymium	Nd	144.24
9	Fluorine	F	18.9984	61	Promethium	Pm	(147)
10	Neon	Ne	20.179	62	Samarium	Sm	150.4
11	Sodium	Na	22.9898	63	Europium	Eu	151.96
12	Magnesium	Mg	24.305	64	Gadolinium	Gd	157.25
13	Aluminium	Al	26.9815	65	Terbium	Tb	158.9254
14	Silicon	Si	28.086	66	Dysprosium	Dy	162.50
15	Phosphorus	P	30.9738	67	Holmium	Ho	164.9303
16	Sulphur	S	32.06	68	Erbium	Er	167.26
17	Chlorine	Cl	35.453	69	Thulium	Tm	168.9342
18	Argon	Ar	39.948	70	Ytterbium	Yb	173.04
19	Potassium	K	39.102	71	Lutetium	Lu	174.97
20	Calcium	Ca	40.08	72	Hafnium	Hf	178.49
21	Scandium	Sc	44.9559	73	Tantalum	Ta	180.9479
22	Titanium	Ti	47.90	74	Tungsten	W	183.85
23	Vanadium	V	50.9414	75	Rhenium	Re	186.2
24	Chromium	Cr	51.996	76	Osmium	Os	190.2
25	Manganese	Mn	54.9380	77	Iridium	Ir	192.2
26	Iron	Fe	55.847	78	Platinum	Pt	195.09
27	Cobalt	Co	58.9332	79	Gold	Au	196.9665
28	Nickel	Ni	58.71	80	Mercury	Hg	200.59
29	Copper	Cu	63.546	81	Thallium	Tl	204.37
30	Zinc	Zn	65.37	82	Lead	Pb	207.2
31	Gallium	Ga	69.72	83	Bismuth	Bi	208.9806
32	Germanium	Ge	72.59	84	Polonium	Po	210
33	Arsenic	As	74.9216	85	Astatine	At	210
34	Selenium	Se	78.96	86	Radon	Rn	222
35	Bromine	Br	79.904	87	Francium	Fr	223
36	Krypton	Kr	83.80	88	Radium	Ra	226.0254
37	Rubidium	Rb	85.4678	89	Actinium	Ac	227
38	Strontium	Sr	87.62	90	Thorium	Th	232.0381
39	Yttrium	Y	88.9059	91	Protactinium	Pa	231.0359
40	Zirconium	Zr	91.22	92	Uranium	U	238.029
41	Niobium	Nb	92.9064	93	Neptunium	Np	237.0482
42	Molybdenum	Mo	95.94	94	Plutonium	Pu	242
43	Technetium	Tc	98.9062	95	Americium	Am	243
44	Ruthonium	Ru	101.07	96	Curium	Cm	247
45	Rhodium	Rh	102.9055	97	Berkelium	Bk	247
46	Palladium	Pd	106.4	98	Californium	Cf	251
47	Silver	Ag	107.868	99	Einsteinium	Es	254
48	Cadmium	Cd	112.40	100	Fermium	Fm	253
49	Indium	In	114.82	101	Mendelevium	Md	256
50	Tin	Sn	118.69	102	Nobelium	No	254
51	Antimony	Sb	121.75	103	Lawrencium	Lw	257
52	Tellurium	Te	127.60				

(b) In alphabetical order

Element	Symbol	Atomic number	Relative atomic mass	Element	Symbol	Atomic number	Relative atomic mass
Actinium	Ac	89	227	Mercury	Hg	80	200.59
Aluminium	Al	13	26.9815	Molybdenum	Mo	42	95.94
Americium	Am	95	243	Neodymium	Nd	60	144.24
Antimony	Sb	51	121.75	Neon	Ne	10	20.179
Argon	Ar	18	39.948	Neptunium	Np	93	237.0482
Arsenic	As	33	74.9216	Nickel	Ni	28	58.71
Astatine	At	85	210	Niobium	Nb	41	92.906
Barium	Ba	56	137.34	Nitrogen	N	7	14.0067
Berkelium	Bk	97	247	Nobelium	No	102	254
Beryllium	Be	4	9.01218	Osmium	Os	76	190.2
Bismuth	Bi	83	208.9806	Oxygen	O	8	15.994
Boron	B	5	10.81	Palladium	Pd	46	106.4
Bromine	Br	35	79.904	Phosphorus	P	15	30.9738
Cadmium	Cd	48	112.40	Platinum	Pt	78	195.09
Calcium	Ca	20	40.08	Plutonium	Pu	94	242
Californium	Cf	98	251	Polonium	Po	84	210
Carbon	C	6	12.011	Potassium	K	19	39.102
Cerium	Ce	58	140.12	Praseodymium	Pr	59	140.0977
Cesium	Cs	55	132.9055	Promethium	Pm	61	147
Chlorine	Cl	17	35.453	Protactinium	Pa	91	231.0359
Chromium	Cr	24	51.996	Radium	Ra	88	226.0254
Cobalt	Co	27	58.9332	Radon	Rn	86	222
Copper	Cu	29	63.546	Rhenium	Re	75	186.2
Curium	Cm	96	247	Rhodium	Rh	45	102.905
Dysprosium	Dy	66	162.50	Rubidium	Rb	37	85.47
Einsteinium	Es	99	254	Ruthenium	Ru	44	101.07
Erbium	Er	68	167.26	Samarium	Sm	62	150.35
Europeium	Eu	63	151.96	Scandium	Sc	21	44.956
Fermium	Fm	100	253	Selenium	Se	34	78.96
Fluorine	F	9	18.9984	Silicon	Si	14	28.086
Francium	Fr	87	223	Silver	Ag	47	107.868
Gadolinium	Gd	64	157.25	Sodium	Na	11	22.9898
Gallium	Ga	31	69.72	Strontium	Sr	38	87.62
Germanium	Ge	32	72.59	Sulfur	S	16	32.06
Gold	Au	79	196.9665	Tantalum	Ta	73	180.948
Hafnium	Hf	72	178.49	Technetium	Tc	43	98.9062
Helium	He	2	4.0026	Tellurium	Te	52	127.60
Holmium	Ho	67	164.9303	Terbium	Tb	65	158.9254
Hydrogen	H	1	1.008	Thallium	Tl	81	204.37
Indium	In	49	114.82	Thorium	Th	90	232.0381
Iodine	I	53	126.9045	Thulium	Tm	69	168.9342
Iridium	Ir	77	192.2	Tin	Sn	50	118.69
Iron	Fe	26	55.847	Titanium	Ti	22	47.90
Krypton	Kr	36	83.80	Tungsten	W	74	183.85
Lanthanum	La	57	138.9055	Uranium	U	92	238.029
Lawrencium	Lw	103	257	Vanadium	V	23	50.9414
Lead	Pb	82	207.2	Xenon	Xe	54	131.30
Lithium	Li	3	6.941	Ytterbium	Yb	70	173.04
Lutetium	Lu	71	174.97	Yttrium	Y	39	88.9059
Magnesium	Mg	12	24.305	Zinc	Zn	30	65.37
Manganese	Mn	25	54.9380	Zirconium	Zr	40	91.22
Mendelevium	Md	101	256				

Compounds, Molecules and Stoicheiometry

We can express the composition of a compound by a *formula* which shows the kind and relative number of atoms in the compound. For example, the formula NaCl for sodium chloride, common salt, shows that sodium chloride is made by combination of sodium and chlorine atoms in equal numbers. The formula $CaCl_2$ for calcium chloride shows that in this compound calcium and chlorine atoms have combined in a ratio of one to two.

Sodium chloride and calcium chloride are typical of *ionic compounds*, which consist of ions regularly arranged in a giant lattice. In such compounds (which we shall discuss in more detail in Units 8 and 9), we cannot distinguish an individual molecule; rather we have to regard each solid particle as one giant molecule composed of a vast number of ions. As you have seen in the diagram of the structure of sodium chloride shown in Figure 8 of Unit 5, it is not possible to distinguish an individual molecule of NaCl. This is in contrast to *covalent compounds*, most of which do exist as individual molecules. The hydrogen molecule H_2, the chlorine molecule Cl_2, the water molecule H_2O, are examples of such covalent molecules. Other covalent molecules are carbon dioxide CO_2, acetylene C_2H_2, and benzene C_6H_6.

The composition of covalent molecules is expressed by a *molecular formula* (a molecule is defined as the smallest portion of a substance capable of existing independently and retaining the properties of the original substance) which shows the kind and actual numbers of atoms present in a molecule of the compound.

molecular formula

Thus the formula CO represents a molecule of a compound (carbon monoxide) which contains one atom of carbon combined with one atom of oxygen. The formula CO_2 represents a molecule of a compound (carbon dioxide) which contains one atom of carbon combined with two atoms of oxygen; $CaCO_3$ is the molecular formula of a compound containing one atom of calcium, one atom of carbon and three atoms of oxygen.

Note particularly that a molecular formula relates to a *compound*. For example, the compound carbon monoxide, a molecule of which is symbolized as CO, is quite different from a *mixture* of carbon and oxygen. Carbon monoxide is a colourless gas which burns with a blue flame and is poisonous, whereas a mixture of carbon and oxygen would be a mixture of a black powder (or of graphite or of diamond, both of which are forms of carbon) and a colourless gas which does not itself burn although it will support burning, and is *essential* for life.

Note also that 2CO means two molecules of carbon monoxide and that the molecular formula shows the actual numbers of each atom present in the molecule. The gas acetylene has a molecular formula C_2H_2 showing that its molecule contains two atoms of carbon and two atoms of hydrogen; $3C_2H_2$ means three molecules of acetylene. C_6H_6 means *one* molecule of a substance (benzene) which contains six atoms of carbon and six atoms of hydrogen.

Groups

We sometimes find a group of atoms which is present in a series of compounds and which maintains its identity in spite of chemical changes in the rest of the compound. An example is the group $-SO_4$ which is known as a sulphate group. Aluminium forms a sulphate which has the molecular formula $Al_2S_3O_{12}$, but since it can be shown that it contains three sulphate groups the molecular formula is usually written $Al_2(SO_4)_3$. Other such groups are seen in the examples below:

$CaCO_3$	Calcium carbonate
Na_2CO_3	sodium carbonate
$NaHCO_3$	sodium hydrogen carbonate
K_2SO_3	potassium sulphite
$MgSO_3$	magnesium sulphite
NH_4Cl	ammonium chloride
$(NH_4)_2CO_3$	ammonium carbonate

Stoicheiometry

The formula of a compound can be used to give us important information about the composition of the compound.

Consider the formula $CaCO_3$ which we saw previously is the formula for calcium carbonate. The relative atomic mass of calcium is 40.08, of carbon (as the normal mixture of isotopes) is 12.011 and of oxygen is 15.999. The relative molecular mass* of calcium carbonate (which is the sum of the relative atomic masses of all the atoms which comprise the formula) is therefore

$$40.08 + 12.011 + (3 \times 15.999) = 100.088$$

From this we can see that the percentage of calcium in calcium carbonate is

$$\frac{40.08 \times 100}{100.088} = 40.05$$

the percentage of carbon is

$$\frac{12.011 \times 100}{100.088} = 12.00$$

the percentage of oxygen is

$$\frac{(3 \times 15.999) \times 100}{100.088} = 47.95$$

If we heat some calcium carbonate (chalk) very strongly in a furnace at a temperature of about 1 500° C it breaks down to give quicklime and the gas carbon dioxide—this is the process known as lime burning. Quicklime is known chemically as calcium oxide.

We can express this change through the *chemical equation*

chemical equation

$$CaCO_3 \rightarrow CaO + CO_2$$

In such equations it is important to realize that the numbers and types of atoms in the molecules on each side of the arrow sign are the same—in the particular example above there are one calcium atom, one carbon atom and three oxygen atoms on each side of the arrow sign. Such an equation is called a *balanced* equation.

---

* The term 'relative molecular mass', although correct, has not supplanted the older equivalent term molecular weight. The definition of relative molecular mass (or 'molecular weight') is the mass of one molecule of a compound relative to that of one atom of $^{12}_{6}C$ taken as 12 exactly.

Balanced equations are not only important because they show the starting materials (always on the left-hand side of the arrow) and the products, but because they also express a *quantitative relationship*. If we write the formula masses under each component:

$$CaCO_3 \rightarrow \quad CaO \quad + \quad CO_2$$
$$100.088 \quad 40.08 + 15.999 \quad \quad 12.011 + (2 \times 15.999)$$
$$= 56.079 \quad \quad \quad = 44.009$$

This says that 100.088 atomic mass units of calcium carbonate gives 56.079 atomic mass units of calcium oxide (quicklime) and 44.009 atomic mass units of carbon dioxide. Since the mass units are the same throughout the equation we can replace them by other mass units and we can for example say that: 100.088 kg of calcium carbonate on heating gives 56.079 kg of calcium oxide and 44.009 kg of carbon dioxide.

> Suppose you wished to make 10 kg of quicklime, how much chalk would you need to heat? How much CO_2 would be produced?

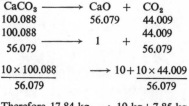

$$CaCO_3 \longrightarrow CaO \quad + \quad CO_2$$
$$100.088 \quad \quad 56.079 \quad \quad 44.009$$
$$100.088 \quad \quad \quad \quad \quad 44.009$$
$$\overline{56.079} \longrightarrow 1 \quad + \quad \overline{56.079}$$

$$\frac{10 \times 100.088}{56.079} \longrightarrow 10 + \frac{10 \times 44.009}{56.079}$$

Therefore 17.84 kg $\longrightarrow$ 10 kg + 7.85 kg
chalk   quicklime carbon
dioxide

The mole

You will remember (section 6.2.4) that the number of atoms of the ^{12}C isotope in exactly 12 g of ^{12}C is known as Avogadro's constant (N_A) and is equal to 6.0225×10^{23}. A mole of any substance is the Avogadro constant of particles of that substance. Thus a mole of chlorine molecules would be 6.022×10^{23} chlorine molecules, a mole of carbon tetrachloride would be 6.022×10^{23} molecules of carbon tetrachloride.

As we saw in section 6.2.4, a mole of ^{12}C atoms has a mass of 12 g. A mole of chlorine atoms of relative atomic mass 35.453 will therefore have a mass of 35.453 g, a mole of chlorine *molecules*, Cl_2, will have a mass of 70.906 g, because each particle in this case will consist of two chlorine atoms. Similarly a mole of carbon dioxide molecules has a mass of 43.999 g, and 100.73 g of calcium carbonate is a mole of calcium carbonate. A mole of any compound is equal to the *gram-formula* of that compound.

> (a) The relative atomic mass of sulphur is 32.06. What would be the mass of a mole of sulphur atoms?
>
> (b) If sulphur existed as the molecule S_8, what would be the mass of a mole of such molecules?
>
> (c) A mole of calcium chloride $CaCl_2$ consists of
>
> ....mole(s) of calcium ions and
>
> ....mole(s) of chloride ions.
>
> (d) What is the mass of 0.1 mole of ethanol, C_2H_5OH?

(a 32.06 g
(b) 8×32.06 g $= 256.48$ g
(c) one mole of calcium ions and two moles of chloride ions
(d) 3.4 g

Appendix 3

The Mass Spectrometer Equation

Derivation of the equation $\dfrac{m}{ne} = \dfrac{B^2 r^2}{2V}$

When an ion of charge ne moves with a velocity v in a plane perpendicular to a magnetic field B, then the force F_β on that ion will be

$$F_\beta = ne\,v\,B$$

If the ion has mass m moves in an orbit of radius r then there will be a centrifugal force F_c on it such that

$$F_c = mv^2/r$$

If the field is uniform the ion will move on an orbit of constant radius r where r is given by the condition $F_\beta = F_c$, i.e.

$$ne\,v\,B = \frac{mv^2}{r}$$

so

$$\frac{m}{ne} = \frac{r\,v\,B}{v^2} = \frac{r\,B}{v}$$

The velocity v depends on the accelerating potential V. The energy gained by an ion carrying a charge ne, after being accelerated by a potential V, will be neV; this will be equal to the kinetic energy. So, supposing that we may legitimately neglect relativistic effects:

$$neV = \tfrac{1}{2}\,mv^2$$

or

$$v^2 = \frac{2neV}{m}$$

Previously we had shown that

$$\frac{m}{ne} = \frac{r\,B}{v}$$

Hence

$$\left(\frac{m}{ne}\right)^2 = \frac{r^2 B^2}{v^2}$$

$$= \frac{m\,r^2 B^2}{2neV}$$

Therefore

$$\frac{m}{ne} = \frac{r^2 B^2}{2V}$$

Where

m is in kilogrammes
e is in coulombs
B is in teslas
r is in metres
V is in volts.

Mass spectrometers may be operated in various ways. If the magnetic field B is kept constant and the ions are brought to focus at a fixed slit (r constant), then the mass of the ion is clearly related to the accelerating potential V. In the mass spectrograph, in which the ions are detected photographically, the magnetic and electrical fields are kept constant and the mass of the ion is then directly related to r^2. In some high precision instruments the electrical and magnetic fields can be varied or held constant independently.

Appendix 4 (Black)

Wave Numbers

The variable in the equation

$$v = f\lambda$$

that can be most accurately measured for electromagnetic radiation is the wavelength. However, it is the frequency that is directly related to the energy. As a consequence spectroscopists usually quote their values as the reciprocal of the wavelength called the *wave number* and represented by σ, that is

wave number

$$\sigma = \frac{1}{\lambda}$$

If λ is measured in centimetres, σ is measured in centimetres^{-1}, and is the number of waves in 1 centimetre. Then the energy is given by $E = hc\sigma$. If σ is in cm^{-1} (as is usual), c (the speed of light) has to be in cm s^{-1}.

Appendix 5

Balmer's Formula

Balmer discovered that the wavelengths of the lines in the visible hydrogen spectrum could be fitted to a mathematical equation:

$$\sigma = \frac{n_1^2}{n_1^2 - 4} \, G$$

where $n_1 = 3, 4, 5, \ldots$
and G is a constant.

The equation is now generally written in the form

$$\sigma = \frac{1}{\lambda} = R\left(\frac{1}{2^2} - \frac{1}{n_1^2}\right)$$

where R is called the Rydberg constant and has the value
$1.097\ 373\ 1 \times 10^7 \ m^{-1}$

The frequency of any line in the Balmer series will then be given by

$$f = Rc\frac{1}{2^2}\left(-\frac{1}{n_1^2}\right)$$

where c is the speed of light.

If the 2 in the Balmer formula is replaced by $n_2 = 1, 2, 3, \ldots$ and n_1 is allowed values $n_2 + 1$, $n_2 + 2$, $\ldots$, we get other series of values for λ or for each value of n_2. For $n_2 = 1$ we get

$$\frac{1}{\lambda} = R\left(\frac{1}{1^2} - \frac{1}{n_1^2}\right)$$

where $n_1 = 2, 3, 4, \ldots$

and the wavelengths obtained are the values for the Lyman series in the far ultra-violet.

If you put $n_2 = 3$ you get

$$\frac{1}{\lambda} = R\left(\frac{1}{3^2} - \frac{1}{n_1^2}\right)$$

where $n_1 = 4, 5, 6, \ldots$

and the values obtained are those of the Paschen series in the infra-red.

The wavelengths of all the lines in the total hydrogen spectrum can be obtained from the general formula which could be written

$$\frac{1}{\lambda} = \frac{R}{n_2^2} - \frac{R}{n_1^2}$$

quite generally, then, the wavelength of any spectral line can be represented by an equation of the type

$$\frac{1}{\lambda} = T_2 - T_1$$

and it is from this that we get the idea of the electron 'jumping' from one level to another and hence the idea of specific energy levels.

(Where a question is not explicitly asked, you are expected to select the correct statement(s) from the set given)

Section 6.1.2

Question 1 (*Objective 1*)

The term 'atomic diameter' means:

(a) the diameter of the atomic nucleus;

(b) the distance between atoms when they are combined together in molecules;

(c) the diameter of an imaginary sphere inside which an atom could just fit;

(d) the distance between atoms when they are packed together in solids.

Question 2 (*Objective 1*)

The charge on the electron is numerically:

(a) greater than that on a proton;

(b) smaller than that on a proton;

(c) the same as that on a proton.

Question 3 (*Objective 1*)

The Rutherford scattering experiment, in which a thin film of gold was bombarded with α particles, shows:

(a) that gold can form very thin films;

(b) that gold has a much greater relative atomic mass than helium;

(c) that gold atoms are largely empty space;

(d) that nearly all the mass of the gold atom is concentrated in a small nucleus.

Section 6.1.4

Question 4 (*Objective 1*)

Which atomic particle is said to have

(a) unit positive charge? . . . .

(b) unit negative charge? . . . .

(c) no charge? . . . .

Question 5 (*Objective 1*)

The term 'nucleon' refers to:

(a) the protons;

(b) the neutrons;

(c) the protons and neutrons;

(d) the protons, neutrons and electrons.

Question 6 (*Objective 4*)

The chemical behaviour of an atom is determined predominantly by:

(a) the number of electrons in an atom of the element;

(b) the density of the element;

(c) the effective size of the atom;

(d) the atomic number of the element;

(e) the number of protons in the nucleus of an atom of the element.

Question 7 (*Objective 1*)

The atomic number of an element is the same as:

(a) the number of nucleons in one atom of the element;

(b) the number of electrons in one atom of the element;

(c) the number of protons in one atom of the element;

(d) the number of neutrons in one atom of the element.

Question 8 (*Objective 4*)

Chemical reactions involve:

(a) transfer of electrons;

(b) transfer of protons;

(c) sharing of electrons;

(d) sharing of protons.

Section 6.1.5

Question 9 (*Objective 1*)

The atoms of a chemical element all have:

(a) the same relative atomic mass;

(b) the same number of nucleons in the nucleus;

(c) the same atomic number.

Section 6.1.6

Question 10 (*Objective 6*)

List the three commonest substances in the Earth's atmosphere:

(a) ....

(b) ....

(c) ....

Section 6.2.3

Question 11 (*Objective 1*)

The relative atomic mass of a nuclide X is:

(a) the mass of one atom of X divided by the mass of one atom of hydrogen;

(b) the mass of one atom of X divided by the mass of one atom of ^{12}C;

(c) the mass of one atom of X divided by the mass of 12 atoms of ^{12}C;

(d) the mass of 12 atoms of X divided by the mass of one atom of ^{12}C;

(e) numerically equal to the mass in kg of 6.022×10^{23} atoms of ^{12}C;

(f) numerically equal to the mass in g of 6.022×10^{23} atoms of ^{12}C;

(g) numerically equal to the mass in g of 6.022×10^{23} atoms of the nuclide X.

Section 6.2.4

Question 12 (*Objective 1*)

Avogadro's number is:

(a) the number of atoms of any nuclide in one atomic mass unit of that nuclide;

(b) the number of atoms of any nuclide in an amount of it in grams numerically equal to its relative atomic mass;

(c) the number of ^{12}C atoms in 12 grams of ^{12}C;

(d) the number of atomic mass units in one gram of anything whatsoever;

(e) approximately the number of water molecules in 18 g of water.

Section 6.2.5

Question 13 (*Objective 2*)

The relative atomic mass of chlorine is given in Appendix 1 as 35.453. This indicates that:

(a) there is probably more than one isotope of chlorine present in a normal sample of chlorine;

(b) if there are two isotopes and one is ^{35}Cl, then the other must have an atomic mass greater than 35;

(c) if the second isotope is ^{37}Cl, then there must be more of it than ^{35}Cl.

Question 14 (*Objective 2*)

The chemical combination method of determining relative atomic masses has a number of limitations. Which of the following statements would you say describe such limitations?

(a) Not every atom combines with carbon;

(b) some atoms do not combine with any others;

(c) errors are liable to be cumulative;

(d) weighing is not an accurate way of measuring things;

(e) it is difficult to eliminate impurities;

(f) the method does not allow for binding energies and this can make big differences to the results.

Section 6.3.4

Question 15 (*Objective 2*)

$^{87}_{37}Rb$ decays into $^{87}_{38}Sr$. What sort of radiation would you expect it to emit in the process?

....

Section 6.4.2

Question 16 (*Objectives 1, 2*)

Which of the following statements would be relevant to answering the question 'What causes the dispersion of light?':

(a) the path of light bends on passing from one medium to another;

(b) light consists of different wavelengths;

(c) the velocity of light of given frequency differs from medium to medium;

(d) the velocity of light depends on the wavelength in media other than a vacuum;

(e) c is always the same no matter how measured;

(f) the frequency of light does not depend on the medium.

Section 6.4.5
(also 6.4.3, 6.4.4)

Question 17 (*Objectives 1, 12*)

Indicate the type of spectrum (1–6 below) you would expect to see if you looked at the following with a hand spectroscope (more than one answer may be required).

(a) a sodium lamp

(b) white light through an atomic vapour

(c) diffuse daylight

(d) a tungsten filament bulb

(1) line spectrum

(2) emission spectrum

(3) continuous spectrum

(4) solar spectrum

(5) atomic spectrum

(6) absorption spectrum

Section 6.5.2
(also 6.4.5, 6.4.6, 6.5.1)

Question 18 (*Objectives 12, 16*)

Which arrow in the energy-level diagram on the right indicates:

(a) an emission process;

(b) an absorption process.

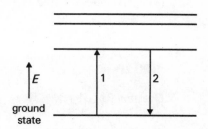

Section 6.5.5
(also 6.5.4)

Question 19 (*Objective 1*)

The term 'principal quantum number' refers to:

(a) the number of electrons which can be excited by any one particular wavelength of electromagnetic radiation;

(b) the number of electrons in a given energy level;

(c) the restrictions on the energy values which an atom can possess;

(d) the number of the energy levels in the hydrogen atom;

(e) none of the above.

Section 6.5.6

Question 20 (*Objectives 1, 17*)

The ionization energy of a hydrogen atom is:

(a) the energy difference between the ground state and the $n=7$ energy level;

(b) the largest energy between consecutive energy levels;

(c) the minimum energy required to remove an electron from its ground state;

(d) the limiting energy of the energy levels E_∞;

(e) the biggest possible energy jump in the Balmer series.

Sections 6.4, 6.5

Question 21 (*Objectives 12, 13, 15, 18*)

An electron in a hydrogen atom has as its principal quantum number $n=3$. Answer the following questions by reference to the text, and your Figure 9.

(a) What is the smallest amount of energy the electron can lose?

(b) What is the frequency of the spectral line involved?

(c) Is this an emission or absorption line?

(d) What series of lines does this one belong to?

(e) What energy would be required to ionize this electron before it loses its energy in (a)?

Appendix 3

Question 22 (*Objective 5*)

Balance the following equations by writing down the lowest values of x, y and z in:

(a) $x\ NaOH + y\ H_2SO_4 \rightarrow Na_2SO_4 + 2H_2O$
    $x = \ldots\ldots\ y = \ldots\ldots$

(b) $x\ CaCO_3 + y\ HCl \rightarrow CaCl_2 + CO_2 + H_2O$
    $x = \ldots\ldots\ y = \ldots\ldots$

(c) $x\ C_2H_6O + y\ O_2 \longrightarrow z\ CO_2 + H_2O$
    $x = \ldots\ldots\ y = \ldots\ldots\ z = \ldots\ldots$

Self-Assessment Answers and Comments

Question 1
Answer (c)

Question 2
Answer (c)

Question 3
Answer (c) (d)

Question 4
Answer (a) proton (b) electron (c) neutron

Question 5
Answer (c)

Question 6
Answer (a)

Comment
Answers (d) and (e) are acceptable only if they are given together with answer (a).

Question 7
Answer (b) (c)

Comment
Since an atom of an element is electrically neutral (b) and (c) give the same number.

Question 8
Answer (a) (c)

Comment
Chemical reactions do not involve the nucleus.

Question 9
Answer (c)

Comment
An element can exist in isotopic forms which have different numbers of nucleons in the nucleus and so different relative atomic masses. All isotopes of an element, however, have the same atomic number.

Question 10
Answer (a) nitrogen
       (b) oxygen
       (c) water vapour
       (d) carbon dioxide

Question 11

Answer   (d)   (g)

Question 12

Answer   (b)   (c)   (e)

Comment

The relative atomic mass of water (H_2O) is approximately 18, so 18 g of water will contain approximately Avogadro's number of water molecules.

Question 13

Answer   (a)   (b)

Comment

The relative atomic mass of any nuclide is always very nearly an integer.

Question 14

Answer   (b)   (c)   (e)

Question 15

Answer β-radiation

Comment

Note that the atomic number has risen by one, whereas the mass number stays the same.

Question 16

Answer   (c)   (d)

Comment

The thing that *causes* dispersion, that is the separation of light of different frequencies, is the fact that the velocity of light in transparent media other than a vacuum is different for different frequencies. *All the other statements are true.* (a) and (b) are relevant to the phenomenon of dispersion. (a) is a result of (c) and there would be nothing to disperse if (b) were not true. But they are not the *cause* of dispersion.

Question 17

Answer   (a) 1, 2, 5

Comment

The sodium lamp gives out the specific lines of the sodium atom spectrum. This is in the form of discrete lines. It is a lamp and so is *emitting* energy.

Answer   (b) 6 (1, 5)

Comment

If white light is passed through an atomic vapour, the vapour absorbs the energy of its atomic spectrum, so it is an absorption spectrum. The absorption consists of dark lines and so could be described as a line absorption spectrum; also, as the dark lines are in fact (part of) an atomic spectrum, it could be described as an atomic absorption spectrum.

Answer   (c) 4, 6 (1)

Comment

The daylight is, of course, a solar spectrum and consists of white light with the absorption lines from the atomic vapours in the sun's atmosphere, so it is an absorption spectrum. As in (b) it *could* be described as a line absorption spectrum.

Answer   (d) 3

Comment

This is the only continuous spectrum on the list and would contain no absorption lines.

Question 18

Answer   (a) 2   (b) 1

Comment

1   An arrow going from the ground state to a higher energy level represents a 'jump' involving the electron gaining energy, so energy has to be added and is absorbed by the electron.
2   An arrow going to a lower energy level represents the electron losing energy. This is given out as a photon and hence is an emission process.

Question 19

Answer   (e)

Comment

The principal quantum number (n) of an energy level is the number given to that energy level by labelling the energy levels with integers starting with the lowest labelled $n=1$. None of the answers is the same as this. In (d) the number of energy levels will be infinite as your graph (Figure 12), in fact, implies. The nearest answer to the correct one is (c), but n is not the restriction but results from the energies being restricted, so in a way (c) results in the energy levels and hence in the principal quantum number.

Question 20

Answer   (c)   (d)

Comment

(c) is the definition of ionization energy, but this is the same as (d), as you saw by the method you used to determine the ionization energy for hydrogen. (e) is not the ionization energy because the electron starts or finishes in the $n=2$ energy level whereas the $n=1$ energy level is the ground state.

Question 21

Answer   (a) 3.027×10^{-19} J

Comment

n cannot change by less than 1, so the electron can lose energy and go to the level with $n=2$. The $n=3$ level is 19.367×10^{-19} J, and the $n=2$ is 16.340×10^{-19} J; so the smallest energy the electron can lose is 3.027×10^{-19} J.

Answer   (b) $f=4.568 \times 10^{14}$ Hz

Comment

$E = hf$, so $f = \dfrac{E}{h}$ and $h = 6.626 \times 10^{-34}$ J s. So the electron jump results in a spectral line of $f = \dfrac{3.027 \times 10^{-19}}{6.626 \times 10^{-34}} = 4.568 \times 10^{14}$ Hz. You could also have obtained this answer by looking at Table 1.

Answer   (c) emission

Comment

The electron is losing energy and this energy is emitted as a photon resulting in an emission line.

Answer   (d) the Balmer series

Comment

It is the Balmer series that results in jumps to the $n = 2$ level.

Answer   (e) 2.37×10^{-19} J

Comment

The ionization energy of the hydrogen atom is 21.74×10^{-19} J (section 6.5.6), and as this electron started in the $n = 3$ energy level with 19.37×10^{-19} J it only needs $(21.74 - 19.37) \times 10^{-19}$ to ionize it.

Question 22

Answer   (a) $x = 2$ $y = 1$
    (b) $x = 1$ $y = 2$
    (c) $x = 1$ $y = 3$ $z = 2$

Answers to in-text Questions

Answer 1 (Q. p. 19)

$^{12}_{6}C$ has 6 neutrons, $^{13}_{6}C$ has 7, and $^{14}_{6}C$ has 8.

Answer 2 (Q. p. 21)

Carbon tetrafluoride contains only carbon and fluorine, hence, if it contains 13.6 per cent of carbon, it contains 86.4 per cent of fluorine (total 100 per cent). Hence 12 g of carbon combines with $\dfrac{12 \times 86.4}{13.6} = 76.2$ g of fluorine. This represents 4 atoms of fluorine and so the relative atomic mass of fluorine in 19.

Answer 3 (Q. p. 21)

Tin dioxide contains 78.8 per cent of tin and by difference 21.2 per cent of oxygen. Hence 32 g of oxygen (remember that tin dioxide has two atoms of oxygen for each atom of tin) combines with $\dfrac{32 \times 78.8}{21.2} = 118.9$ g of tin and so the relative atomic mass of tin is 118.9.

Answer 4 (Q. p. 28)

$^{226}_{88}Ra$

Answer 5 (Q. p. 28)

$^{87}_{37}Rb$

Notes

Notes

The Open University

Science Foundation Course Unit 7

THE ELECTRONIC STRUCTURE OF ATOMS

Prepared by the Science Foundation Course Team

THE OPEN UNIVERSITY

Contents

Table A

A List of Scientific Terms, Concepts and Principles used in Unit 7

Taken as pre-requisites			Introduced in this Unit			
1	**2**		**3**		**4**	
Assumed from general knowledge	Introduced in a previous Unit	Unit No.	Developed in this Unit	Page No.	Developed in a later Unit	Unit No.
	atomic spectrum	6	electronic structure	7		
	energy levels	6	successive ionization energies	7		
	ionization energy	6	electron energy shells	9		
	ground state	6	electron energy sub-shells	15		
	electron	2	azimuthal quantum number (l)	15		
	atomic number	6	s, p, d, f nomenclature	18		
	quantum number	6	electronic configuration	18		
	principal quantum number (n)	6	electron spin	20		
	Coulomb Law	4	pairing of electron spins	20		
	proton	6	Hund's rule	21		
	neutron	6	unpaired electrons	21		
			Periodic Table	26		

Objectives

When you have completed the work for this Unit, you should be able to:

1 Define, or recognize adequate definitions of, or distinguish between true and false statements concerning each of the terms, concepts and principles in column 3 of Table A (p. 5).

2 Explain (1) by writing short statements or (2) by selecting items from a list, the following features of a graph of first ionization energies versus atomic number:

(a) major peaks;

(b) the arrangements of the points before each major peak;

(c) the division into electronic energy shells.

3 Given a general energy-level diagram and a particular element's atomic number, determine the electronic configuration of the element (only up to atomic number 38), and show the electronic configuration by (a) drawing arrows in boxes, (b) writing in s, p nomenclature, or (c) selecting from examples of either.

4 Show the first ionization energies of an element on an energy-level diagram, given the element's atomic number.

5 Explain the features of the Periodic Table in terms of electronic configuration.

6 Describe, in general terms, a direct method of determining ionization energies by electron impact. (TV programme.)

Introduction

We have developed the energy-level diagram for hydrogen from the atomic spectrum in some detail (Unit 6). The same type of procedure could lead to the energy-level diagram for other atoms. However, with more than one electron in an atom the atomic spectrum becomes more complex. While the actual electronic structure of an atom can only be confirmed experimentally by interpreting the spectrum, a certain amount of knowledge can be gained just from examining ionization energies. This is what we propose to do.

We shall examine ionization energies and build up the energy-level diagrams for other atoms and introduce rules to enable you to work out the electronic structures of the atoms of most elements. We develop this facility so that you can go on in Unit 8 to examine the chemical properties of elements in the light of their electronic structures.

If you have trouble following the development you will find the procedures summarized at the end of section 7.2.1, at the start of 7.2.3 and again at the end of 7.4. The structures are compared and collected together in section 7.5 which is the direct lead into the chemistry in Unit 8.

Table 1

Ionization Energy	Energy (joule)
1st	8.20×10^{-19}
2nd	75.71×10^{-19}
3rd	115.30×10^{-19}
4th	158.37×10^{-19}
5th	222.27×10^{-19}
6th	275.76×10^{-19}
7th	333.41×10^{-19}
8th	423.01×10^{-19}
9th	479.97×10^{-19}
10th	$2\,340.80 \times 10^{-19}$
11th	$2\,648 \quad \times 10^{-19}$

7.1 Many Electron Atoms

In Unit 6 you saw, for the particular case of hydrogen, how the atomic spectrum of an element can be interpreted in terms of electron 'jumps' between specific energy levels and from these energy levels (obtained from the spectrum) you obtained (by extrapolation) the value of the ionization energy.

Remind yourself of the definition of ionization energy.

We want to extend our knowledge to other elements and then relate the information on the arrangements of the electrons in atoms (called their *electronic structure*) to the chemistry of the elements.

The ionization energy (see section 6.5.6) is the minimum energy required to ionize an electron from its ground state. The ground state is the lowest possible energy level that the electron can occupy (see section 6.5.2).

electronic structure

The full interpretation of the atomic spectra of elements other than hydrogen is beyond this Foundation Course but you will see that quite a lot of useful information can be obtained from the ionization energies of the elements. In particular we will show that the electronic structure of the elements show periodic variations with atomic number that are reflected (as will be shown in Unit 8) in their chemical properties. By the time we reach this point we will have introduced further quantum numbers.

Do you remember what a quantum number is? (cf. 6.5.5)

7.1.1 Successive ionization energies

Look again now at the cover of this Course Book. As mentioned earlier, it is obvious that other atomic spectra are more complex than the hydrogen spectrum. You can probably see regularities in the iron spectrum.

We introduced the principal quantum number n as a method of *numbering* the energy levels in hydrogen so that each value of n was associated with a particular energy (level).

Can you think of any reason why the spectra of other elements are more complex than that of hydrogen? Consider helium with two electrons in each atom. Think about the Coulomb Law forces that would be present in the atom.

Consider sodium, its atomic number is 11 so the sodium atom has 11 electrons around it and we could imagine removing all these electrons one at a time.

In the helium atom there will be Coulomb Law attractive forces between the nucleus and each of the two electrons, but there will also be Coulomb Law repulsions between the two electrons. It is these repulsions that will make the spectra of many electron atoms more complex.

Would you expect the energies required to remove all these eleven electrons to be the same? Can you think of one reason for your answer?

As you probably realize the energies are different. After one electron is removed there are still 11 positive charges in the nucleus, but now there are only 10 electrons so there are less repulsion terms.

Table 1 lists the energies required successively to remove all the electrons from the sodium atom. These are called the *successive ionization energies* for sodium. For example having removed one electron the energy required to remove the next one is called the second ionization energy and is 75.71×10^{-19} joule for sodium.

successive ionization energies

Do you observe any striking features in this table?

Clearly the first electron is much more easily removed than any others and also the last two electrons are very much more tightly held than all the others.

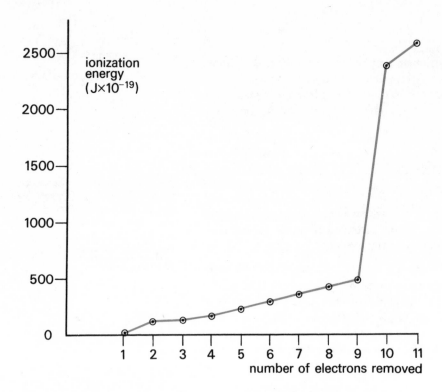

Figure 1

Successive ionization energies for sodium.

A graph of these values (Fig. 1) is no more revealing than the table. It shows that each successive electron requires more energy to remove it and that in sodium the electrons fall into three groups. The first electron is relatively easy to remove and the last two are very difficult. Neither from the table nor the graph is it immediately clear whether or not the energies required to remove the other eight electrons increase in a regular manner (second to ninth ionization energies).

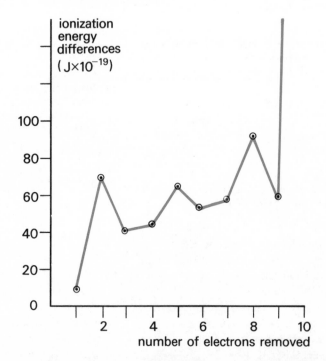

Figure 2

Increase in ionization energies for sodium.

If the extra energy required to remove each electron (second ionization energy minus first ionization energy, for example) is plotted, as shown in Figure 2, the question is easily answered.

List any deductions you think you can make from Figure 2.

Again, the most obvious feature is that there are three groups of electrons, the first electron removed being different from the next eight and the last two being in a third group. Now, however, it is clear that the energies required to remove the second to ninth electron respectively do not increase in a regular manner, far from it. The significance of the variations is not obvious and the variations cannot be interpreted without considerably greater information.

7.1.2 Electron energy shells

Concentrate on the obvious features of the table and the graphs. These groups of electrons (containing for sodium one, eight and two electrons respectively) are called *electron shells*. The most easily removed electron is held with the smallest force by the nucleus and is in the outer-most electron shell of the sodium atom. Conversely the last two electrons removed are most firmly bound and are in the inner-most electron shell of the sodium atom. This could be represented by Figure 3 where the circles represent electrons.

electron shells

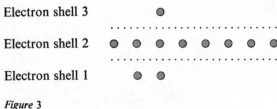

Electron shell 3

Electron shell 2

Electron shell 1

Figure 3

Electron energy shells for sodium.

If the electron shells are numbered, starting with the inner-most shell numbered 1, then the sodium atom has two electrons in its first electron shell, eight in the second shell and one in the third shell. These numbers for the electron shells are the principal quantum numbers (n) and correspond to the numbers you have already used for the energy levels of the hydrogen atom.

How many electrons in the sodium atom have principal quantum number $n=2$?

Eight.
$n=2$ refers to the second electron shell and in a sodium atom there are eight electrons in this shell.

Lists of successive ionization energies for the atoms of other elements would reveal the same type of shell structure of the electrons. As for sodium the first shell would be found to contain two electrons (at the most) and the second shell up to eight electrons. *The electron shells for atoms of different elements correspond to each other.*

7.1.3 Variations of first ionization energies

Table 2 lists the first ionization energies (I.E.) for the first twenty elements —listed in order of atomic number.

Plot the first ionization energy as a function of atomic number on Figure 4. The first three points are given. List any features of the plot that strike you.

Your plot should look like Figure 5 (p. 13)

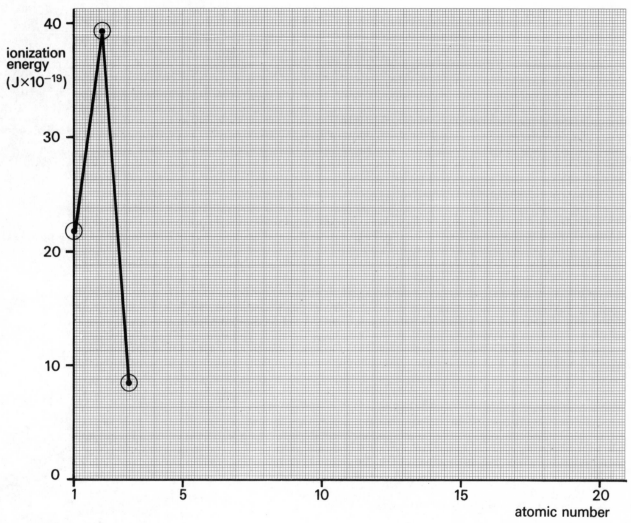

Figure 4

Ionization energy versus atomic number.

Table 2

Atomic Number	I.E. (joule)
1 (H)	21.74×10^{-19}
2 (He)	39.38×10^{-19}
3 (Li)	8.61×10^{-19}
4 (Be)	14.93×10^{-19}
5 (B)	13.26×10^{-19}
6 (C)	18.06×10^{-19}
7 (N)	23.27×10^{-19}
8 (O)	21.81×10^{-19}
9 (F)	27.92×10^{-19}
10 (Ne)	34.52×10^{-19}
11 (Na)	8.20×10^{-19}
12 (Mg)	12.22×10^{-19}
13 (Al)	9.59×10^{-19}
14 (Si)	13.06×10^{-19}
15 (P)	16.81×10^{-19}
16 (S)	16.60×10^{-19}
17 (Cl)	20.84×10^{-19}
18 (Ar)	25.21×10^{-19}
19 (K)	6.95×10^{-19}
20 (Ca)	9.79×10^{-19}

In looking at the values in Table 2 or at the points on your plot, you are comparing the elements in order of increasing atomic number. That is, going from one element to the next an extra electron is also added. The table and plot compare the energy required to remove the least tightly held electron from the atoms of different elements. In the last section we said that the electron shells in different atoms were comparable. Then, the last electron added in building one atom from another in this way is probably the least tightly bound electron.

If this is so you should be able to compare this step-by-step building (starting with hydrogen) up to sodium with the finished sodium atom. That is, the first ionization energy of all the atoms up to sodium might be expected to show the same features as the successive ionization energies of sodium.

Look at your plot from hydrogen to sodium and compare this with Figure 2. Are they comparable?

They are certainly both jagged but for comparable features see the following text.

If you look for groups, look at the numbers of elements in your plot as it builds up to the peaks. By the time you get to sodium you should have groups of two, eight and one, with the one representing the first ionization energy of sodium itself. These look like the numbers we obtained from the successive ionization energy plot but in reverse. They are not really in reverse, as the one in each case is the most easily removed electron of the sodium atom. The groups come reversed, because in your plot you are building from the inner electrons and in Figure 2 the plot starts from the outer-most electron.

As this building process goes on by adding protons (and of course any neutrons required) the electrons added go into the inner-most available electron shell.

How many electrons at most can
(a) the first electron shell hold?
(b) the second electron shell hold?

Figure 6 shows Figures 2 and 5 with dotted lines separating electron energy shells.

From Figure 2 and your plot (Fig. 4) the answers are

(a) 2

(b) 8

Figure 6

Plots 2 and 5 showing electron energy shells.

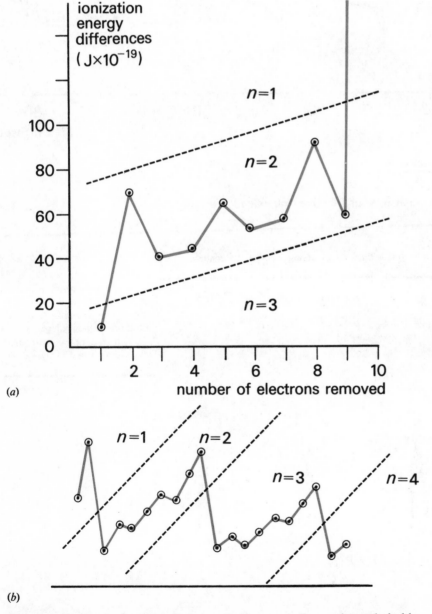

(a)

(b)

From Figure 6 (b) it looks as if the $n=3$ electron shell can also only hold eight electrons.

11

7.1.4 Ionization energies up to radon

Before considering the third electron shell further, let us see whether the repetitive behaviour found up to atomic number 20 is repeated beyond

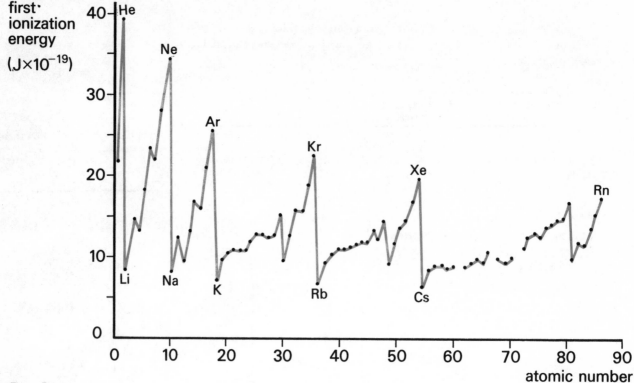

Figure 7

Ionization energy versus atomic number to 86.

there. Figure 7 shows a plot similar to your Figure 4, but extended up to atomic number 86.

Do any of the features that you noticed up to atomic number 20 continue beyond there? List them.

The arrangement of the eight points preceding each major peak are very

The major peaks continue and each is followed by a point in the minimum position. You probably also noticed similarities in the arrangements of the points leading up to each maximum. These are discussed in the following text.

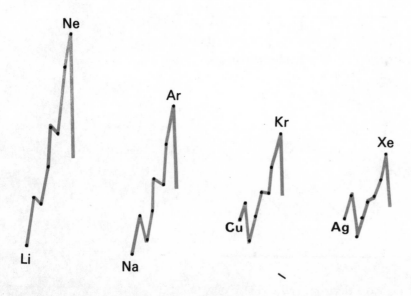

Figure 8

Some groups from Figure 7.

12

similar. These points are separated out in Figure 8 (the points are incomplete for the part of the graph leading up to radon).

Looking at these groups in increasing atomic number, you see two points, then three, followed by a further three. The arrangement of the points is very similar though getting less distinct with increasing atomic number. You will see the reason for these similarities later. For the moment neglect these finer features and imagine the graph divided up as in Figure 6. If you count the number of elements in each group, leading from a minimum to the next peak (as we did in section 7.1.3), you get groups of 2, 8, 8, followed by 18, 18 and 32, though not all the ionization energies in the last group are known, some of the elements do not occur naturally but have been 'made' artificially.

By using the procedure you used in section 7.1.3, you might deduce that the electron shells would hold 2, 8, 8, 18, 18 and 32 electrons respectively, and that these groups would have principal quantum numbers 1, 2, 3, 4, 5 and 6. Radon would thus have 8 electrons with principal quantum number $n=3$, 18 electrons with $n=4$, 18 with $n=5$, and 32 with $n=6$.

In fact, the above procedure for grouping the elements does not give correct results beyond atomic number 20. A detailed analysis of atomic spectra shows that, of the 18 electrons in the fourth group, 10 have principal quantum number $n=3$, that is, they are actually in the third electron shell, which thus can hold not 8 but *18* electrons.

The maximum number of electrons that can be associated with any particular value of the principal quantum number n are actually given by the formula $2n^2$. Thus for $n=1$, the maximum number of electrons is 2, and so on.

For $n=2$ the maximum number of electrons $=8$

$n=3$ the maximum number of electrons $=18$

$n=4$ the maximum number of electrons $=32$

Thus we have 2, 8, 18, 32 respectively (not 2, 8, 8, 18, 32, 32 as the grouping procedure above suggested).

Can these numbers be accounted for? Yes, but to do so we should have to introduce three more quantum numbers. Think back for a moment to the hydrogen atom. Here, with only one electron in each atom, the value of the principal quantum number is sufficient to define the energy of the electron with respect to the nucleus. However, for atoms with many electrons this is no longer so. For example, carbon has four electrons with

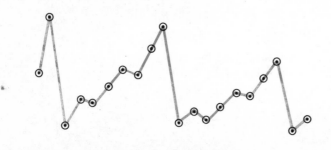

Figure 5

Ionization energy versus atomic number to 20. Compare with your plot (Figure 4).

principal quantum number 2. The successive ionization energies for carbon are in Table 3, and are plotted in Figure 9.

Table 3   Successive Ionization Energies for Carbon (J)

1st	2nd	3rd	4th
18.06×10^{-19}	39.04×10^{-19}	77.1×10^{-19}	102.8×10^{-19}
	5th	6th	
	628.7×10^{-19}	791.9×10^{-19}	

When you look at Figure 9, remember that, as in Figure 1, plots of successive ionization energies show the points representing removal of the least tightly bound electrons first. These will have the highest values of n. Points representing the removal of electrons with $n=1$ will then occur last.

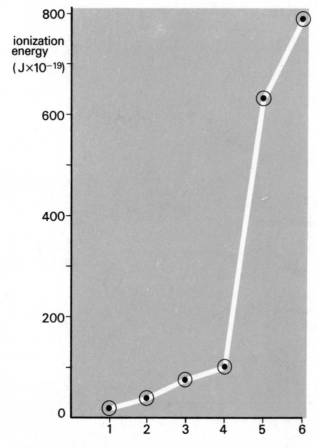

Figure 9

Successive ionization energies for carbon.

Figure 9 clearly shows the two different electron shells, the lower four points representing electrons in the second shell (having $n=2$). The fifth and sixth electrons removed clearly belong to a different energy shell.

14

7.2 Energy sub-shells

7.2.1 The azimuthal quantum number

The different energies of the electrons in a particular electron quantum shell are explained by postulating the existence of sub-shells and to characterize these sub-shells another quantum number is introduced. This is called the *azimuthal quantum number* and is designated by the letter l.

electron energy sub-shells

azimuthal quantum number

Like the principal quantum number, n, for our purposes l can be regarded as a counting procedure and it only has whole number values. For theoretical reasons the lowest value l is given is 0. So l can be 0, 1, 2, etc. In carbon there are two sub-shells in the quantum shell with $n=2$ and there are two electrons in each sub-shell. Look at Figure 8 again. You can see a difference between the two sub-shells. However, this is NOT generally true in all elements.

Look at your plot of first ionization energies versus atomic number. (Fig. 4.)

How many sub-shells do you think there are in the $n=2$ shell and how many electrons in each?

It looks from the figure as if there are three sub-shells containing respectively, two, three and three electrons. However, this is not correct—see following text.

The actual number of sub-shells cannot be determined from ionization energy data. It can be obtained from the atomic spectrum or from theoretical considerations, both of which methods are beyond us here. The values that l can take depend on the value of n, that is the number of sub-shells in each electron shell depends on the quantum number of that electron shell (the principal quantum number). The values that l can have are 0, 1, 2, etc. to a maximum of $n-1$.

What are the possible values of l for electrons in:
(a) the first electron shell
(b) the second electron shell
(c) the third electron shell?

(a) for $n=1$, as l can only be $n-1$ as a maximum, there is only one possible value of l, i.e. $l=0$

(b) for $n=2$, l can be 0 and 1, so there are two sub-shells

Do you have sufficient information to determine the maximum possible number of electrons in the $n=1$, $l=0$ energy level?

(c) for $n=3$, l can be 0, 1 or 2, so there are three sub-shells.

Look at your ionization energy versus atomic number plot (Fig. 4) and the plot of successive ionization energies for sodium (Fig. 1) and at the plot successive ionization energies for carbon (Fig. 9). All these give you the answer to the question, how many electrons can be in the $n=1$, $l=0$ level?

The $n=1$, $l=0$ level is the closest to the nucleus, that is it contains the most strongly bound electrons. These are represented by the first two (left-hand) points in Figure 5 and the last two points in Figures 1 and 9. In all these plots it is clear that the maximum number of electrons in this level is 2. In your first ionization energy plot, this shell was filled at helium and the next electron (at lithium) went into the $n=2$ quantum shell.

What you have just noticed about the $n=1$, $l=0$ energy level is true about all sub-shells designated by $l=0$: they can hold a maximum of two electrons.

How many electrons can be in a sub-shell with $l=1$?

You could use the same type of argument, referring to Figure 7, to show that the maximum number of electrons in a sub-shell denoted by $l=2$ is 10.

The rules for determining the number of sub-shells, that is the number of possible values of l for any given value of n, also tell us the number of energy levels in an atom. Each different energy level is characterized by the value of the two quantum numbers n and l.

Here (Fig. 10 (a)), as a reminder, is the energy-level diagram for the hydrogen atom. In a ground state atom the electron is in the lowest energy level and is here represented by a circle.

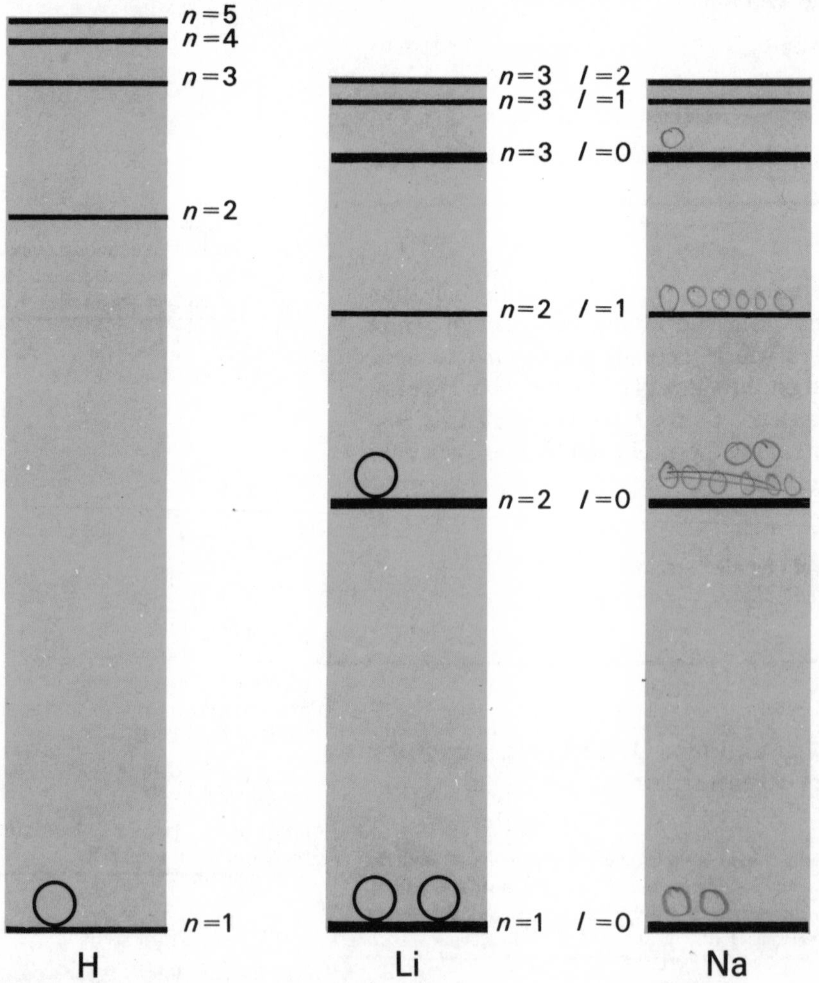

Did you realize that you had enough information to answer this? Look at your first ionization energy versus atomic number plot and at the plot of the successive ionization energies for sodium to obtain the answer, which is below.

There can be 8 electrons in the $n=2$ quantum shell and the possible values of l are 0 and 1. As there can only be two electrons in an $l=0$ level, there clearly can be 6 in an $l=1$ level.

H
(a)

Li
(b)

Na
(c)

Figure 10

Energy-level diagrams (a) H, (b) Li, (c) Na.

Figure 10 (b) is an energy-level diagram for the lithium atom (the diagrams are NOT to scale*). The lithium atom contains three electrons. In the ground state they will be in the lowest possible energy levels and are

* *We have not drawn the energy-level diagrams to scale because they would either be too large or too cramped. For example, the diagram for lithium, if drawn to scale, would show the distance between* n=1, l=0 *and* n=2, l=0 *about ten times as large as that between the* n=2, l=0 *and* n=3, l=0 *levels.*

16

represented by circles on the figure. Figure 10 (c) is a similar diagram for sodium (atomic number 11).

> **Using circles, place the electrons in appropriate places in Figure 10 (c) to represent the electronic arrangement of a ground state sodium atom. If you aren't sure how to go about this, re-read this section.**

At this stage you should be able to give the electronic structure of the atoms of any element up to atomic number 20, and beyond this point if you were given the appropriate energy-level diagrams. Here is a summary of the information you would use.

(a) In a ground state atom the electrons fill the lowest energy levels first.

(b) The values of the energy levels are determined first by the principal quantum number n; the lower values of n have lower energies (with respect to the nucleus).

(c) n can have the values 1, 2, 3, etc.

(d) The principal quantum number designates the electron shells: these are divided into sub-shells denoted by the azimuthal quantum number, l.

(e) The number of sub-shells is determined by the number of possible values of l.

(f) l can have values 0, 1, 2, etc. to a maximum of $n-1$.

(g) In atoms with more than one electron sub-shells with higher values of l have higher energies (we have not said this explicitly above but it is implied by our counting procedure).

(h) An $l=0$ sub-shell can contain two electrons, an $l=1$ sub-shell can contain six electrons, and an $l=2$ sub-shell can contain ten electrons.

Figure 11 represents the energy-level diagrams for boron, aluminium and neon (NOT to scale).

> **Look up your list of atomic numbers (Unit 6, Appendix 1) and, using circles to represent electrons as in Figure 10, indicate the electronic structure of these elements.**

The number of electrons in each level for each element is given in this table:

n	1	2		3		
l	0	0	1	0	1	2
B	2	2	1			
Al	2	2	6	2	1	
Ne	2	2	6			

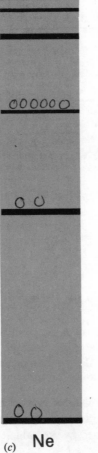

$n=3 \quad l=2$
$n=1 \quad l=3$
$n=3 \quad l=0$

$n=2 \quad l=1$

$n=2 \quad l=0$

$n=1 \quad l=0$

(a) **B**   (b) **Al**   (c) **Ne**

Figure 11

Energy-level diagrams (a) B, (b) Al, (c) Ne.

17

7.2.2 s, p, d, f nomenclature

We should now introduce the standard nomenclature for the values of l. Because, historically, the lines of one of the series in the sodium spectrum were first seen as 'sharp' and of another series as 'diffuse', but a third series was regarded as the 'principal' series in the spectrum, the values of the azimuthal quantum number l are usually denoted by the initial letters s, p, d, f (where f came from 'fundamental') instead of numbers:

$$
\begin{aligned}
&\text{s for sub-shells with } l=0 \\
&\text{p for sub-shells with } l=1 \\
&\text{d for sub-shells with } l=2 \\
&\text{f for sub-shells with } l=3
\end{aligned}
$$

These letters can then be used as a short method of writing the electronic structure or *configuration* of atoms. The electron in a ground state hydrogen atom has principal quantum number $n=1$ and azimuthal quantum number $l=0$, which is represented by s. So it is said to be in a 1s energy level and the electronic configuration of the ground state hydrogen atom is written

$$1s.$$

For helium there are two electrons with $n=1$ and $l=0$. That is two 1s electrons. This is shown by using a superscript on the s, so the electronic configuration of helium is $1s^2$.

Lithium has two electrons in this same energy level and its third electron has $n=2$, $l=0$, and is in a 2s level. The electronic structure of lithium is then $1s^2$, $2s^1$ where the superscript ^{1} shows that there is one electron in the 2s level.

Using this procedure show the electronic configuration for

(a) sodium

(b) boron

(c) aluminium.

(Look back to the question in section 7.2.1 for help if you need it.)

This nomenclature can also be used on an energy-level diagram. The diagram for fluorine would be as shown in Figure 12.

Indicate the electron configuration for fluorine by using circles as in section 7.2.1 on Figure 12.

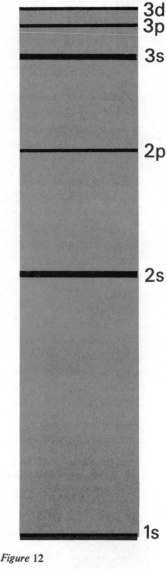

Figure 12

Energy-level diagram for F.

(a) Na has 2 electrons in the $n=1$, $l=0$; 2 in the $n=2$, $l=0$; 6 in the $n=2$, $l=1$ level; and 1 in the $n=3$, $l=0$ level, so it is shown as $1s^2$, $2s^2$, $2p^6$, $3s^1$.

(b) B is similarly $1s^2$, $2s^2$, $2p^1$.

(c) Al is $1s^2$, $2s^2$, $2p^6$, $3s^2$, $3p^1$.

The electronic configuration for fluorine (atomic number 9) is $1s^2$, $2s^2$, $2p^5$ so the levels will have 2, 2 and 5 circles reading from the bottom.

7.2.3 Electronic configuration of elements

As we have said above, given the appropriate energy-level diagram, you should be able to write the electronic configuration for the ground state atoms of any element using the sp nomenclature. The procedure you would use would be as follows:

(a) the atomic number of the element gives the number of electrons;

(b) from section 7.2.1, you know the maximum number of electrons in any energy level (determined by the value of l);

(c) place the electrons in the energy-level diagram, *filling* the lowest energy levels first.

Figure 13 shows the energy-level diagrams for oxygen, sulphur and selenium.

Write the electronic configuration for oxygen, sulphur and selenium.

For O—$1s^2$, $2s^2$, $2p^4$

  S—$1s^2$, $2s^2$, $2p^6$, $3s^2$, $3p^4$

  Se—$1s^2$, $2s^2$, $2p^6$, $3s^2$, $3p^6$, $3d^{10}$, $4s^2$, $4p^4$.

There are two important points to notice about these exercises.

(1) The 3d electron level for selenium lies *above* the 4s energy level and hence the 4s level is filled first. This phenomenon of the d level being higher than the succeeding s level is generally true.

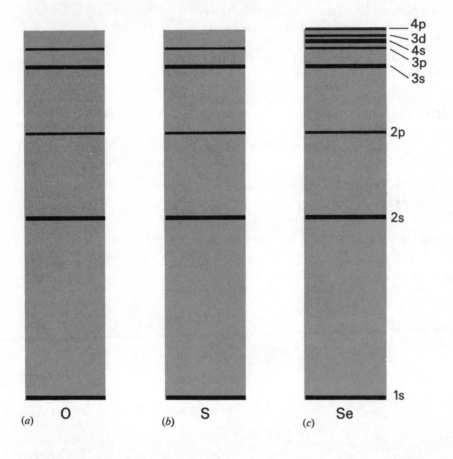

Figure 13

Energy-level diagrams O, S, Se.

(a) O   (b) S   (c) Se

(2) The other thing to notice is that these three elements all have their least tightly bound electron in a p sub-shell containing 4 electrons (p^4).

You are now in a position to group the elements on the basis of their electronic configuration. Some questions may, however, be worrying you.

(1) Why, in hydrogen, is it necessary to consider only the principal quantum number (n) to explain the spectrum?

(2) In most elements, why does the 3d level appear *above* the 4s level?

(3) Is there any explanation for the (magic?) numbers 2, 6, 10, 14 which are the maximum number of electrons in s, p, d and f energy levels?

(4) What can be said about the position of the electrons relative to the nucleus when they are in the various energy levels?

These questions are in fact to some extent related, but an understanding of the answers to them is not necessary for the next steps in our argument, so they are discussed in Appendix 2 (Black).

19

7.3 Electron Spin

Before we go on to group the elements, we will introduce another method of representing electronic structures. This recognizes an important property of electrons which was not discovered until 1925.

Electrons behave in some ways as if they were charged spheres, spinning in much the same way as the Earth or a gyroscope spins. However, electrons can only have two possible ways of 'spinning'. You could think of these of clockwise and anti-clockwise. Electrons with opposite spins form stable pairs. The main importance of electron spin for an understanding of chemical reactions is this property of pairing. The electrons in each sub-shell can be divided into pairs so that a filled p sub-shell that contains six electrons has three pairs.

The electronic structure of the atoms in an element can be represented by showing each electron as a small arrow, pointing the arrows up or down to represent the two possible spins of the electrons. The electronic structure of helium is $1s^2$ and hence has one pair of electrons and would be represented on this system as

1s

$\boxed{\uparrow\downarrow}$

Sodium with an electronic structure $1s^2\,2s^2\,2p\;\,3s^1$ would be represented as

1s	2s	2p	3s
$\boxed{\uparrow\downarrow}$	$\boxed{\uparrow\downarrow}$	$\boxed{\uparrow\downarrow}\boxed{\uparrow\downarrow}\boxed{\uparrow\downarrow}$	$\boxed{\uparrow}$

Notice that one box is used for each electron pair so a p sub-shell has three boxes allowing three pairs.

7.4 Hund's Rule

Note that we have single boxes for 1s and 2s levels, as there is only one pair of electrons, and a triple box for 2p to allow for the three possible pairs.

Use this system to show the electronic structure of argon.

A d sub-shell can contain ten electrons, i.e. five pairs, and is represented by a five-compartment box.

The electronic structure of argon is $1s^2$, $2s^2$, $2p^6$, $3s^2$, $3p^6$ and so is

	1s	2s	2p	3s	3p
Ar	↑↓	↑↓	↑↓ ↑↓ ↑↓	↑↓	↑↓ ↑↓ ↑↓

Now try selenium. Refer back to Figure 13 for the energy-level diagram.

You should have been faced with a dilemma when you attempted to put the arrows in your 4p boxes. Is there any way of deciding whether to write

4p
| ↑↓ | ↑ | ↑ |

or

4p
| ↑↓ | ↑↓ | |

?

That is, should the electrons be *paired*, as on the right, or be left unpaired if possible, as on the left?

This is resolved by *Hund's Rule*, which says that there will be the maximum number of unpaired electrons consistent with filling the lowest energy levels first. The left-hand version is correct in this case.

Now, with this rule, you should be able to write the electronic structure of the atoms of any element, given its energy-level diagram.

The electronic structure from Figure 13 is $1s^2 2s^2 2p^6 3s^2 3p^6 3d^{10}$, $4s^2 4p^4$, so the structure is represented as

	1s	2s	2p	3s	3p
Se	↑↓	↑↓	↑↓ ↑↓ ↑↓	↑↓	↑↓ ↑↓ ↑↓

3d	4s	4p
↑↓ ↑↓ ↑↓ ↑↓ ↑↓	↑↓	↑↓ ↑ ↑

For comment on this see the following main text.

Hund's Rule

Show the electronic structure of ground state atoms of phosphorus, strontium, cobalt and silver, using both the $1s^2$, etc. and the box method. Use the energy-level diagram in Figure 13 (c). Remember to fill the lowest energy levels, irrespective of quantum number, first.

As you will see, if you did the last problem, there are *still* some snags. Unfortunately, there are no rules to give you the answer in these cases that don't follow Hund's rule. In atoms with many electrons, as you can see from Figure 13 (c), the energies of the outer energy levels are sometimes very close together indeed, and occasionally the presence of electrons in, say, the 4d energy level changes the relative position of the 5s level, so that sometimes it holds two electrons and sometimes only one. We know this from experiments.

The structures are:

P $\quad 1s^2 2s^2 2p^6 3s^2 3p^3$

	1s	2s	2p	3s	3p
	↑↓	↑↓	↑↓ ↑↓ ↑↓	↑↓	↑ ↑ ↑

Sr $\quad 1s^2 2s^2 2p^6 3s^2 3p^6 3d^{10} 4s^2$

	1s	2s	2p	3s	3p
	↑↓	↑↓	↑↓ ↑↓ ↑↓	↑↓	↑↓ ↑↓ ↑↓

3d	4s
↑↓ ↑↓ ↑↓ ↑↓ ↑↓	↑↓

Co $\quad 1s^2 2s^2 2p^6 3s^2 3p^6 3d^7 4s^2$

	1s	2s	2p	3s	3p
	↑↓	↑↓	↑↓ ↑↓ ↑↓	↑↓	↑↓ ↑↓ ↑↓

3d	4s
↑↓ ↑↓ ↑ ↑ ↑	↑↓

Can you guess what type of experiment?

This sort of information is obtained from a detailed examination of the atomic spectrum of an element. The analysis of such spectra is too complex for the Foundation Course and will be left until subsequent years.

The electronic structures of all the elements are given in tabular form in Appendix 1 (p. 28).

In this Unit, we have now established a series of rules and procedures for writing the electronic structure of any element, given a general energy-level diagram. These procedures, as you could confirm for yourself if you had time, give the results in Appendix 1 up to atomic number 40, with only two exceptions. These exceptions can, in fact, be found by a quick examination of the appendix.

Run your eyes down the first 3d column. For which element would the procedures we have used give the wrong answer?

The anomalies you would find would not really be exceptions to the rules. If you had the correct energy-level diagram for each element, you would be able to get the correct answer. Clearly, from the anomaly just discussed (Cr), the energies of the configurations

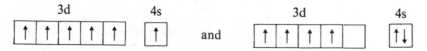

must be very similar. *Knowing* the answer, you could probably think of sensible reasons for it.

You will remember that we have said that the results in Appendix 1 are obtained from a detailed examination of atomic spectra. In Unit 6, you saw how an energy-level diagram could be obtained from a simple spectrum. While this is much more difficult with a complex spectrum such as that of, say, cobalt, the general approach is the same.

Here is a summary of the procedures and rules you would use to write the electronic structures given an energy-level diagram.

1 The atomic number of the element tells you the number of electrons.

2 These electrons are 'fed' into the energy-level diagram using the following rules:

(a) the electrons fill the lowest energy levels first;

(b) the maximum number of electrons have the same spin (Hund's Rule).

3 The number of possible values of the quantum numbers are determined by the rules:

$$n = 1, 2, 3, \text{etc};$$
$$l = 0 \text{ to } n - 1.$$

(You probably no longer apply these last rules, you probably just remember that:

        an s sub-shell can contain 2 electrons, 1 pair;
        a   p sub-shell can contain 6 electrons, 3 pairs;
        a   d sub-shell can contain 10 electrons, 5 pairs.)

Ag $1s^2\ 2s^2\ 2p^6\ 3s^2\ 3p^6\ 3d^{10}\ 4s^2\ 4p^6$
      $4d^{10}\ 5s^1$

If you have understood the preceding material and looked at the examples carefully, you should have all of these correct *except* the last one.

For comment on this see the following main text.

Chromium. Which has only one 4s electron compared with vanadium having two. As a result the 3d sub-shell has five electrons, whereas we might have expected four.

22

We can now summarize the information we have about the number of electrons in various energy levels in the following way:

Energy levels with principle quantum numbers	$n=1$	2	3	4	
can hold . . .	2	8	18	32	electrons

Energy levels (sub-shells) denoted by values of	$l=0$	1	2	3	
are represented by . . .	s	p	d	f	
can hold . . .	2	6	10	14	electrons

This means that a filled $n=4$ electron energy shell has sub-shells represented as

$$4s^2 \; 4p^6 \; 4d^{10} \; 4f^{14}.$$

We should give a warning here about the procedure we are using. You will notice that we are treating the energy-level diagram *as if* the energy level were there *whether the electrons were there or not*. The energy level, of course, only has a real meaning when there is an electron in it. We are also treating the energy levels as if they were fixed whereas the actual energy of an electron depends on the nuclear charge and the other electrons present. So, when we say that two electrons in lithium, say, are in the same energy level (the two 1s electrons), we in no way imply that if one of them is removed (to form in this case the Li^{2+} ion) the energy of the remaining one is unaffected.

The energy-level diagram gives us the energies of the electrons when they are all in the atom; this is why it can be used to 'build up' the electronic structure, as we have been doing here.

7.5 What About Chemistry?

Well, what was the point of all this?

You will remember that we have frequently said that chemical properties are determined by the electrons in an atom. You now have a good knowledge of the electronic structures of atoms of different elements and this is a good basis on which to start discussing chemical properties. This is the task of the next Unit.

Having established the electronic structures, let us return now to Figure 7 (p. 12) and see whether we can make more sense of this now, in the light of a knowledge of electronic structure. Here are the electronic structures up to sodium.

	1s	2s	2p			3s
H	↑					
He	↑↓					
Li	↑↓	↑				
Be	↑↓	↑↓				
B	↑↓	↑↓	↑			
C	↑↓	↑↓	↑	↑		
N	↑↓	↑↓	↑	↑	↑	
O	↑↓	↑↓	↑↓	↑	↑	
F	↑↓	↑↓	↑↓	↑↓	↑	
Ne	↑↓	↑↓	↑↓	↑↓	↑↓	
Na	↑↓	↑↓	↑↓	↑↓	↑↓	↑

Clearly you could expand the information in Appendix 1 in the same sort of way. If you compare the information about electronic structures with Figure 7, you will see that the low points (representing easily removed electrons) are all points where a new electron energy shell (new value of the principal quantum number n) is being started with an s electron. These points represent the electrons:

$$Li \qquad 2s^1$$
$$Na \qquad 3s^1$$
$$K \qquad 4s^1$$
$$Rb \qquad 5s^1$$
$$Cs \qquad 6s^1.$$

Also the peaks, where the first ionization energies are higher and it is most difficult to remove an electron, are all points where the last electron filled a p energy level, for example:

$$Ne \qquad 2p^6$$
$$Ar \qquad 3p^6$$
$$Kr \qquad 4p^6$$
$$Xe \qquad 5p^6$$
$$Rn \qquad 6p^6.$$

You will also notice that a half-filled p sub-shell is associated with stability (that is, it is more difficult to remove an electron), in particular in the lighter elements. For example, nitrogen, with $2p^3$ (hence ⊡⊡⊡), has a higher first ionization energy than oxygen, with a final structure of $2p^4$, and there is a similar effect between phosphorus and sulphur, and between arsenic and selenium, though the effect is decreasing.

Both the table of electronic structures (Appendix 1) and Figure 7 show repetitive or periodic behaviour, and we have pointed out a few obvious examples of this above. You will also expect that similar electronic structures will result in similar chemical properties.

This repetitive behaviour can be shown by grouping the symbols of the elements with similar arrangements of their outer electrons under each other. Up to argon this would be

3	4	5	6	7	8	9	10
Li	Be	B	C	N	O	F	Ne

11	12	13	14	15	16	17	18
Na	Mg	Al	Si	P	S	Cl	Ar

(Note that we are leaving hydrogen and helium out. Hydrogen might logically go over lithium ($1s^2\ 2s^1$), as it is $1s^1$; and helium, with $1s^2$, might go over beryllium, with $1s^2\ 2s^2$, but this is not straightforward and will be discussed in detail in the next Unit.)

You should check that in fact the grouping above is correct on the basis of the electronic structure. Compare one or two pairs by reference to Appendix 1.

If the next line is started, potassium ($4s^1$) will group under sodium, and calcium ($4s^2$) under magnesium; but the element that starts the 4p sub-shell is not the next element, scandium, which is $3d^1\ 4s^2$, but gallium which is $3d^{10}\ 4s^2\ 4p^1$. The intervening elements, with atomic numbers 21 (scandium) to 30 (zinc), have electrons in the 3d energy level. So the correct grouping would be

3	4										5	6	7	8	9	10
Li	Be										B	C	N	O	F	Ne
11	12										13	14	15	16	17	18
Na	Mg										Al	Si	P	S	Cl	Ar
19	20	21	22	23	24	25	26	27	28	29	30	31	32	33	34	35	36
K	Ca	Sc	Ti	V	Cr	Mn	Fe	Co	Ni	Cu	Zn	Ga	Ge	As	Se	Br	Kr

Notice that each row starts with a new value of the principal quantum number. The next line of grouping also fits this pattern, with a few exceptions, because of the fluctuations of the relative positions of the 4d and 5s energy levels which was discussed in section 7.6.

3	4											5	6	7	8	9	10
Li	Be											B	C	N	O	F	Ne
11	12											13	14	15	16	17	18
Na	Mg											Al	Si	P	S	Cl	Ar
19	20	21	22	23	24	25	26	27	28	29	30	31	32	33	34	35	36
K	Ca	Sc	Ti	V	Cr	Mn	Fe	Co	Ni	Cu	Zn	Ga	Ge	As	Se	Br	Kr
37	38	39	40	41	42	43	44	45	46	47	48	49	50	51	52	53	54
Rb	Sr	Y	Zr	Nb	Mo	Tc	Ru	Rh	Pd	Ag	Cd	In	Sn	Sb	Te	I	Xe

Continuing in this same fashion, you would again meet a problem after lanthanum (element with atomic number 57); the next element with a $p^6d^2s^2$ outer structure is not cerium, which starts filling the 4f shell, but hafnium (element 72). So the grouping should now be extended again.

The last line (including the artificially made elements 93 upwards) fits this same pattern. This final arrangement is known as the Periodic Table of the elements (see Table 4).

It is a remarkable fact that the main details of this table were drawn up long before chemists had *any* knowledge of electronic structure and, indeed, before many elements had been discovered. But this fascinating story is for the next Unit.

Table 4   The Periodic Table

3	4														
Li	Be														
11	12														
Na	Mg														
19	20	21													
K	Ca	Sc													
37	38	39													
Rb	Sr	Y													
55	56	57	58	59	60	61	62	63	64	65	66	67	68	69	70
Cs	Ba	La	Ce	Pr	Nd	Pm	Sm	Eu	Gd	Tb	Dy	Ho	Er	Tm	Yb
87	88	89	90	91	92	93	94	95	96	97	98	99	100	101	102
Fr	Ra	Ac	Th	Pa	U	Np	Pu	Am	Cm	Bk	Cf	Es	Fm	Md	No

										5 B	6 C	7 N	8 O	9 F	10 Ne
										13 Al	14 Si	15 P	16 S	17 Cl	18 Ar
	22 Ti	23 V	24 Cr	25 Mn	26 Fe	27 Co	28 Ni	29 Cu	30 Zn	31 Ga	32 Ge	33 As	34 Se	35 Br	36 Kr
	40 Zr	41 Nb	42 Mo	43 Tc	44 Ru	45 Rn	46 Pd	47 Ag	48 Cd	49 In	50 Sn	51 Sb	52 Te	53 I	54 Xe
71 Lu	72 Hf	73 Ta	74 W	75 Re	76 Os	77 Ir	78 Pt	79 Au	80 Hg	81 Tl	82 Pb	83 Bi	84 Po	85 At	86 Rn
103 Lw															

Appendix 1

Electronic Configurations of the Elements

	1s	2s 2p	3s 3p 3d	4s 4p 4d 4f	5s 5p 5d 5f	6s 6p 6d	7s
1 H	1						
2 He	2						
3 Li	2	1					
4 Be	2	2					
5 B	2	2 1					
6 C	2	2 2					
7 N	2	2 3					
8 O	2	2 4					
9 F	2	2 5					
10 Ne	2	2 6					
11 Na	2	8	1				
12 Mg	2	8	2				
13 Al	2	8	2 1				
14 Si	2	8	2 2				
15 P	2	8	2 3				
16 S	2	8	2 4				
17 Cl	2	8	2 5				
18 Ar	2	8	2 6				
19 K	2	8	8	1			
20 Ca	2	8	8	2			
21 Sc	2	8	8 1	2			
22 Ti	2	8	8 2	2			
23 V	2	8	8 3	2			
24 Cr	2	8	8 5	1			
25 Mn	2	8	8 5	2			
26 Fe	2	8	8 6	2			
27 Co	2	8	8 7	2			
28 Ni	2	8	8 8	2			
29 Cu	2	8	8 10	1			
30 Zn	2	8	8 10	2			
31 Ga	2	8	18	2 1			
32 Ge	2	8	18	2 2			
33 As	2	8	18	2 3			
34 Se	2	8	18	2 4			
35 Br	2	8	18	2 5			
36 Kr	2	8	18	2 6			
37 Rb	2	8	18	8	1		
38 Sr	2	8	18	8	2		
39 Y	2	8	18	8 1	2		
40 Zr	2	8	18	8 2	2		
41 Nb	2	8	18	8 4	1		
42 Mo	2	8	18	8 5	1		
43 Tc	2	8	18	8 6	1		
44 Rn	2	8	18	8 7	1		
45 Rh	2	8	18	8 8	1		
46 Pd	2	8	18	8 10			
47 Ag	2	8	18	8 10	1		
48 Cd	2	8	18	8 10	2		
49 In	2	8	18	18	2 1		
50 Sn	2	8	18	18	2 2		
51 Sb	2	8	18	18	2 3		
52 Te	2	8	18	18	2 4		
53 I	2	8	18	18	2 5		
54 Xe	2	8	18	18	2 6		
55 Cs	2	8	18	18	8	1	
56 Ba	2	8	18	18	8	2	
57 La	2	8	18	18	8 1	2	

28

	1s	2s 2p	3s 3p 3d	4s 4p 4d 4f	5s 5p 5d 5f	6s 6p 6d	7s
58 Ce	2	8	18	18 2	8	2	
59 Pr	2	8	18	18 3	8	2	
60 Nd	2	8	18	18 4	8	2	
61 Pm	2	8	18	18 5	8	2	
62 Sm	2	8	18	18 6	8	2	
63 Eu	2	8	18	18 7	8	2	
64 Gd	2	8	18	18 7	8	2	
65 Tb	2	8	18	18 9	8	2	
66 Dy	2	8	18	18 10	8	2	
67 Ho	2	8	18	18 11	8	2	
68 Er	2	8	18	18 12	8	2	
69 Tm	2	8	18	18 13	8	2	
70 Yb	2	8	18	18 14	8	2	
71 Lu	2	8	18	32	8 1	2	
72 Hf	2	8	18	32	8 2	2	
73 Ta	2	8	18	32	8 3	2	
74 W	2	8	18	32	8 4	2	
75 Re	2	8	18	32	8 5	2	
76 Os	2	8	18	32	8 6	2	
77 Ir	2	8	18	32	8 9		
78 Pt	2	8	18	32	8 9	1	
79 Au	2	8	18	32	8 10	1	
80 Hg	2	8	18	32	8 10	2	
81 Tl	2	8	18	32	18	2 1	
82 Pb	2	8	18	32	18	2 2	
83 Bi	2	8	18	32	18	2 3	
84 Po	2	8	18	32	18	2 4	
85 Ar	2	8	18	32	18	2 5	
86 Rn	2	8	18	32	18	2 6	
87 Fr	2	8	18	32	18	8	1
88 Ra	2	8	18	32	18	8	2
89 Ac	2	8	18	32	18	8 1	2
90 Th	2	8	18	32	18	8 2	2
91 Pa	2	8	18	32	18 2	8 1	2
92 U	2	8	18	32	18 3	8 1	2
93 Np	2	8	18	32	18 4	8 1	2
94 Pu	2	8	18	32	18 5	8	2
95 Am	2	8	18	32	18 7	8	2
96 Cm	2	8	18	32	18 7	8 1	2
97 Ek	2	8	18	32	18 8	8 1	2
98 Cf	2	8	18	32	18 10	8	2
99 Es	2	8	18	32	18 11	8	2
100 Fm	2	8	18	32	18 12	8	2
101 Md	2	8	18	32	18 13	8	2
102 No	2	8	18	32	18 14	8	2

The Position of the Electron

You will remember that, in the main text (p. 19), we posed some questions to which we deferred the answers. Here are the questions.

1 Why, in hydrogen, is it necessary to consider only the principal quantum number (n) to explain the spectrum?

2 In most elements why does the 3d level appear *above* the 4s level?

3 Is there any explanation for the (magic?) numbers 2, 6, 10, 14, which are the maximum number of electrons in s, p, d and f energy levels?

4 What can be said about the position of the electrons relative to the nucleus when they are in the various energy levels?

7.A2.1   The hydrogen spectrum

With regard to question 1, the sub-shell structure and the number of values of l, etc. do also apply to hydrogen.

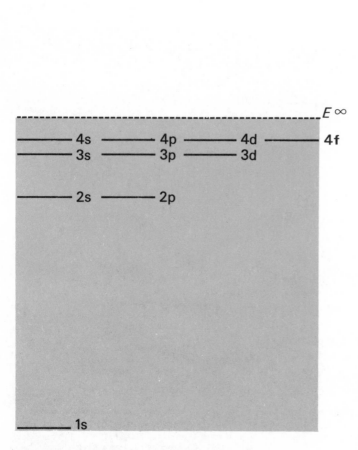

(a) Hydrogen energy level diagram

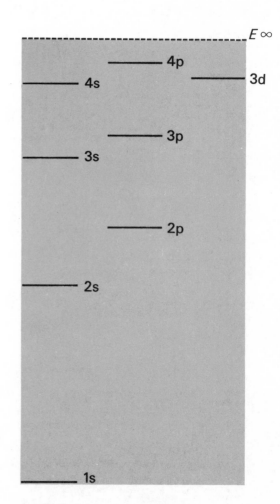

(b) Selenium energy diagram

Figure 14

Energy-level diagram (H and Se).

How does the value of *l* effect the energy level in the hydrogen atom? (Look at Figure 10, p. 16.)

We discussed the difference between hydrogen and other atoms in section 7.1.1 and pointed out that with more than one electron in an atom there would be repulsive forces between the electrons. This is why the energy levels with the same value of *n* but different values of *l* are different, except in hydrogen.

So the hydrogen energy-level diagram could be as given in Figure 14 (a). The energy-level diagram for selenium is given for comparison in Figure 14 (b). Note that the selenium diagram is the same as in Figure 13 (c), p. 19, except that the p, d, etc. sub-shells are displayed for clarity.

Figure 10 shows that the energy levels in hydrogen are just labelled with values of *n*. If the sub-shells exist they all have the same energy, i.e. 2s and 2p are the same energy level in the hydrogen atom. '*l*' *has no influence on the energy level in the hydrogen atom.**

7.A2.2 The 4s and 3d energy levels

The question as to why the 4s energy level, in selenium for example, is below the 3d energy level (question 2 above) is closely related to the question of the position of an electron in these energy levels (question 4 above).

So far we have been deliberately vague about the *position* of the electron with respect to the nucleus as distinct from its *energy*. If you look back you will see that we have suggested (mainly on a general Coulomb Law argument) that the electron will be further from the nucleus the higher the value of *n*, and for the limiting value of ($n = \infty$) the electron will leave the nucleus and the atom become an ion.

The energy of this $n = \infty$ level we have called E_∞, and for hydrogen it is the ionization energy.

Is E_∞ the ionization energy for selenium? Before answering, draw an arrow on Figure 14 representing the energy jump that corresponds to the first ionization energy for selenium and then answer the question.

Your arrow should go from the 4p level to the E_∞ level, as here.

7.A2.3 The position of the electron

Let us return to the position of the electron. The answer to the question 'where is the electron?' poses an important problem that will be dealt with in Unit 30; but the reason for the problem is as follows.

How is the question 'where is the nucleus?' answered? Think back to Unit 6 and the Rutherford experiment. Here a heavy nucleus was bombarded by a light nucleus (a helium nucleus or α-particle) and in effect the experiment determined where the α-particle rebounded to. The nucleus more or less stayed in place on impact, because it was so massive compared with an α-particle. The Rutherford experiment would be no use for studying helium nuclei, let alone electrons.

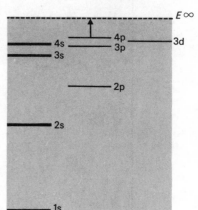

The first ionization energy is the energy required to remove the *least tightly bound* electron. As the 1s level is the lowest energy level and hence has $E = 0$ the size of your arrow represents less energy than E_∞ (less by the energy separating the 1s and 4p levels in this case).

If you can't follow this, try bouncing a marble off:

(a) a cricket ball;

(b) another marble.

You could find out quite a bit about the position and size of the cricket ball by seeing where the 'projectile' marble went, but very little about the stationary marble in (b).

* *Under high resolution the lines in the hydrogen spectrum are split, but this is not solely a result of the value of l (see Unit 30).*

What then could be used to 'look' at an electron? Another electron would merely displace the electron we were looking at. How about a photon of light? You have seen that electrons in an atom can interact with photons of specific energy: the interaction results in absorption (giving an absorption spectrum) of the photon and the electron jumps to another energy level, so by looking at it we change its energy and also presumably its position.

Can nothing, then, be said about the position of the electron? As you can imagine from the above very brief discussion, it will be difficult to obtain direct experimental evidence. However, as you will see later, one of the standard procedures in science can be useful here. A *model* (cf. Unit 1) of the system is devised and predictions from the model are compared with experiments. When dealing with the behaviour of electrons in an atom, a mathematical model is used; it is known as quantum theory and will be discussed later, in Units 29 and 30.

The energy levels, and hence the spectrum, of the hydrogen atom derived from this model agree with those measured experimentally. So scientists consider that deductions from the model about the position of the electron are also likely to be reliable.

7.A2.4 Radial distribution functions

Well, what *does* quantum theory say about the position of an electron in atom? It says that the position of the electron *cannot* be given; what can be given is only a choice of likely positions. We can only state the probability of finding the electron in any given position; we can never state its position with absolute certainty.

The only experimental evidence we can obtain about the shapes of atoms suggests that they are spherical, so the most useful way we can express

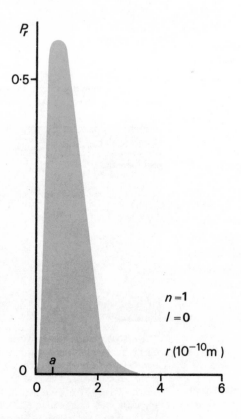

Figure 15

Radial distribution function H (1s).

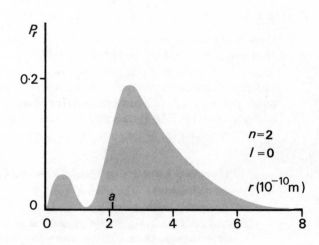

Figure 16

Radial distribution function H (2s).

the results of quantum theory on the position of the electron is in the form of a *radial distribution function*. That is, a function showing how far in any direction from the nucleus an electron is *likely* to be found.

Figure 15 is a graph of the radial distribution function for an electron in the 1s energy level of a hydrogen atom (the ground state). The graph gives the probability P_r (on the ordinate) of finding the electron anywhere in a thin spherical shell of fixed thickness, radius r from the nucleus. (This is equivalent to the probability of finding the electron at the distance r from the nucleus.) Notice that the most likely place to find the electron (shown by the peak of the graph) is about 0.6 Å from the nucleus. But you will also notice that there is still some probability of finding the electron three times as far away. For an electron in the 2s energy level of hydrogen the radial distribution function is as shown in Figure 16.

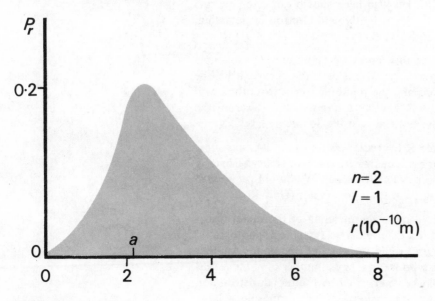

Figure 17

Radial distribution function H (2p).

The radial distribution function depends on l. Again, for hydrogen, the radial distribution function for an electron in a 2p energy level is as shown in Figure 17.

The average distance of the electron from the nucleus, when it is in the various energy levels (2s, 2p, etc.), is marked a on Figures 15–17. This distance is the same for hydrogen 2s and 2p energy levels and, as we said before, the energy of these two levels is the same.

If similar radial distribution functions applied to lithium (they do approximately), then the 2s and 2p levels would have different energies. The radial distribution functions show that an electron in a 2s energy level is more likely to be found close to the nucleus (see the first small peak on Figure 16) than an electron in a 2p energy level. In hydrogen this does not affect the energy, as the average distance is the same, but in lithium there are two electrons in the 1s energy level and the repulsions from these will depend on how close the electron with $n=2$ can get. This results in the 2s and 2p levels having different energies. This effect will be present whenever there is more than one electron in an atom.

The hydrogen 3d and 4s radial distribution functions are given in Figure 18. You can see that in hydrogen the average distance from the nucleus is

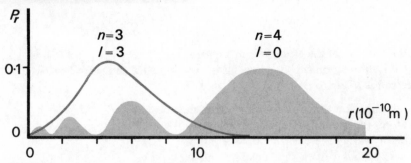

Figure 18

Radial distribution function H (3d and 4s).

greater for electrons in the 4s energy level than the 3d energy level, and so the 4s level has a higher energy than the 3d level, as shown earlier on the energy-level diagram. If similar radial distribution functions applied to potassium, say, where the energy levels up to 3p are filled, the effect of an electron in the 4s energy level being able to spend *some* time closer to the nucleus than in the 3d energy level means that the 4s level will have a lower energy than the 3d. This has also been shown earlier on energy-level diagrams, and results in the least tightly held electron in potassium being in the 4s energy level, not the 3d energy level.

If you are not quite clear about this, don't worry unduly. On a simple picture, you can see that when a 4s electron is near the nucleus it will be closer to it than the 3p electrons and the repulsive forces from these will push it inwards, thus helping the nuclear attraction and lowering the energy. This cannot occur if the electron is in the 3d energy level.

You will have noticed that some of the radial distribution functions show that there are distances from the nucleus where the probability of finding the electron is zero. These regions are called *nodes*. We do not propose to discuss them further at this stage, but shall do so later (Unit 30).

It would perhaps help you to visualize the meaning of the radial distribution function, if you look at it a different way. Imagine a 'photograph' of a hydrogen atom. The electron would be 'seen' at one point. Another 'photo' would show it at another point. In a large number of photographs the distribution of points would be determined by the radial distribution function P_r. The results (in two dimensions) of superimposing a large number of such 'photos' for an electron in the 1s and 2s energy levels of hydrogen are shown in Figure 19. The full relationship between Figure 19 and Figures 15 and 16 we shall again leave until Unit 30.

Figure 19

Electron distribution H (1s and 2s).

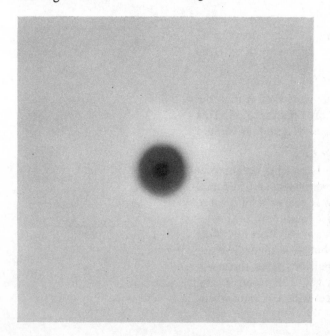
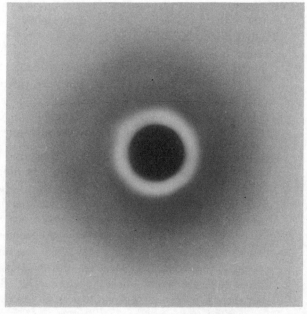

A2.5 The magnetic quantum number

Return now to the third question posed above: is there any explanation of the 'magic' numbers that give the maximum possible number of electrons in any particular energy level as defined by n and l. Here, as a reminder, are the numbers:

Energy level	Maximum number of electrons
1s	2
2s	2
2p	6
3s	2
3p	6
3d	10
4f	14

We can explain these numbers by introducing two more quantum numbers. As before, these were postulated to explain certain features of atomic spectra. If a single line of an atomic spectrum is viewed while the material is in a strong magnetic field, it will be found that the line is split into multiple lines. This effect on two closely spaced lines in the sodium spectrum is shown in Figure 20. It is called the Zeeman effect.

The existence of different lines means that the number of possible energy 'jumps' that the electron can take has increased, and this means that the number of energy levels has increased. We designate the newly formed energy levels by a new quantum number called, appropriately enough, the *magnetic quantum number*, denoted by m. The values that m can take depend on the value of l for the level that has been split by the magnetic field. The values m can take are the whole numbers from $+l$ to $-l$ inclusive.

For $l=0$, m can only be 0;
for $l=1$, m can be 1 or 0 or -1;
for $l=2$, m can be 2, 1, 0, -1 or -2

<u>How many levels will an f energy level be split into in a strong magnetic field?</u>

Even if there is no magnetic field, we can still use the magnetic quantum numbers to label electrons. Different values of m will simply not affect the energy of electrons in the absence of the field.

If you now define energy levels by n, l and m, and *if* you assume that all energy levels so defined can hold the same number of electrons, you can work out the maximum number of electrons in any particular energy level.

<u>How many electrons can there be in an energy level for $n=2$, $l=1$, and $m=1$?</u>

The same type of argument can be used to find the maximum number of electrons in an $n=3$, $l=2$, $m=2$ level.

<u>How many?</u>

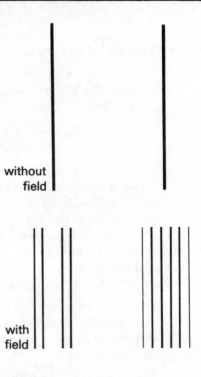

Figure 20

Zeeman effect.

magnetic quantum number

An f energy level (section 7.2.2) is one with $l=3$, so m can be 3, 2, 1, 0, -1, -2, and -3, so there are *seven* energy levels in the magnetic field.

This is a 2p energy level. The possible values of m are: 1, 0 and -1, so there are three energy levels with $n=2$, $l=1$. You already know that the 2p energy levels can contain six electrons, so, as there are three 2p energy levels, each can contain a maximum of *two electrons*.

For 3d energy levels the possible values of m are 2, 1, 0, -1 and -2, so there are five levels and these can hold ten electrons, so in each there can be *two electrons*.

7.A2.6 The 'spin' of an electron

You see that, with this further quantum number, the 'magic' number problem changes from explaining four or more different numbers to explaining one.

__Can you state the new problem?__

The question left is: 'why can two electrons be associated with a particular value of m?'

Again, we appeal to experiment. Many lines in atomic spectra were found under high resolution to be multiple lines even in the absence of a magnetic field (they split into even more lines in a field). For example, the bright yellow line that you yourself observed in the sodium spectrum in Unit 6 is really two lines (called a doublet), and it is these lines that we show split in Figure 20.

The explanation of this *fine structure*, as it is called, is that electrons, whether in atoms or not, have associated with them a property called *spin*. You can think of this as the electron being a sphere and spinning on an axis like the Earth. Electrons can have only two possible spins. You can think of these as clockwise and anti-clockwise.

fine structure

There are only two possible values of the spin, and we introduce a *spin quantum number*, designated by s (not to be confused with the s used for energy levels with $l=0$). The spin quantum number s can have values $+\frac{1}{2}$ or $-\frac{1}{2}$ (the actual value has theoretical significance that we do not propose to discuss here).

spin quantum number

With this further property of the electron and its associated quantum number, we can forget the 'magic numbers' used earlier and rely on a single rule called the *Pauli Principle*. This says that *no two electrons in an atom can have all four quantum numbers the same*.

Pauli Principle

Take an example. For an energy level with $n=1$ and $l=0$, say in helium, there can only be one value of m, that is $m=0$. So the electrons in this energy level can have quantum numbers $n=1$, $l=0$, $m=0$, $s=+\frac{1}{2}$ and $n=1$, $l=0$, $m=0$, $s=-\frac{1}{2}$. Thus, there can be a maximum of two electrons.

You could now construct a table showing the quantum numbers of all the possible electrons in any energy level (Table 5). This shows the case discussed above in tabular form (for $n=1$, $l=0$) and also the values for $n=2$, $l=0$ and $n=2$, $l=1$.

__Complete the space in Table 5 for $n=3$, $l=2$ and $n=4$, $l=3$.__

The completed table is on p. 38.

You will notice, for example, that the fourth electron shell ($n=4$) can hold a maximum of fourteen electrons.

In the text (section 7.3 onwards), the method of indicating the electronic structures of atoms uses a 'box' for each possible value of m and an arrow to represent each electron. The arrows point up and down to represent the possible values of s so each 'box' can contain two arrows to represent one pair of electrons with opposite spins.

Self-Assessment Questions

Section 7.1.1

Question 1 (*Objective 1*)

Why are the spectra of other elements more complex than that of hydrogen? Consider helium with two electrons in each atom. Think about the Coulomb Law forces that would be present in the atom.

Section 7.1.2

Question 2 (*Objective 2*)

How many electrons in the sodium atom have principal quantum number $n=2$?

Section 7.1.3

Question 3 (*Objective 2*)

How many electrons at most can

(a) the first electron shell hold?

(b) the second electron shell hold?

Section 7.2.1

Question 4 (*Objective 2*)

How many electrons can be in the $n=1$, $l=0$ level?

Section 7.4.1

Question 5 (*Objective 3*)

What is the electronic structure of selenium (show by the box representation). Use Figure 13 (c) as the energy-level diagram.

Section 7.4.2

Question 6 (*Objectives 5 and 3*)

Using the rules summarized at the end of section 7.4.2 and Figure 13 (c) as a general energy-level diagram, find the second apparent anomaly in Appendix 1. Suggest an explanation for the anomaly.

n	l	m	s
1	0	0	$+\frac{1}{2}$
			$-\frac{1}{2}$
2	0	0	$+\frac{1}{2}$
			$-\frac{1}{2}$
	1	1	$+\frac{1}{2}$
			$-\frac{1}{2}$
		0	$+\frac{1}{2}$
			$-\frac{1}{2}$
		-1	$+\frac{1}{2}$
			$-\frac{1}{2}$

Table 5

Question 1

Answer

In the helium atom there will be Coulomb Law attractive forces between the nucleus and each of the two electrons but there will also be Coulomb Law repulsions between the two electrons. It is these repulsions that will make the spectra of many electron atoms more complex.

Question 2

Answer 8

Comment

$n=2$ refers to the 2nd electron shell and in a sodium atom there are 8 electrons in this shell.

Question 3

Answer

From Figure 2 and your plot (Figure 4) the answers are
(a) 2
(b) 8

Question 4

Answer 2

Comment

The $n=1$, $l=0$ level is the closest to the nucleus, that is it contains the most strongly bound electrons. These are represented by the first two (left hand) points in Figure 4 and the last two points in Figures 1 and 9. In all these plots it is clear that the maximum number of electrons in this level is 2. In your ionization energy plot this shell was filled at helium and the next electron (at lithium) went into the $n=2$ quantum shell.

Question 5

Answer

The electronic structure from Figure 13 (c) is $1s^2$ $2s^2$ $2p^6$ $3s^2$ $3p^6$ $3p^{10}$ $4s^2$ $4p^4$ so the structure is represented as follows:

Se

1s   2s   2p   3s   3p   3d

$[\uparrow\downarrow]$ $[\uparrow\downarrow]$ $[\uparrow\downarrow|\uparrow\downarrow|\uparrow\downarrow]$ $[\uparrow\downarrow]$ $[\uparrow\downarrow|\uparrow\downarrow|\uparrow\downarrow]$ $[\uparrow\downarrow|\uparrow\downarrow|\uparrow\downarrow|\uparrow\downarrow|\uparrow\downarrow]$

4s   4p

$[\uparrow\downarrow]$ $[\uparrow\downarrow|\uparrow|\uparrow]$

The 4p arrangement is determined by Hund's rule (see text).

n	l	m	s
1	0	0	$+\frac{1}{2}$
			$-\frac{1}{2}$
2	0	0	$+\frac{1}{2}$
			$-\frac{1}{2}$
		1	$+\frac{1}{2}$
			$-\frac{1}{2}$
	1	0	$+\frac{1}{2}$
			$-\frac{1}{2}$
		-1	$+\frac{1}{2}$
			$-\frac{1}{2}$
3	2	2	$+\frac{1}{2}$
			$-\frac{1}{2}$
		1	$+\frac{1}{2}$
			$-\frac{1}{2}$
		0	$+\frac{1}{2}$
			$-\frac{1}{2}$
		-1	$+\frac{1}{2}$
			$-\frac{1}{2}$
		-2	$+\frac{1}{2}$
			$-\frac{1}{2}$
4	3	3	$+\frac{1}{2}$
			$-\frac{1}{2}$
		2	$+\frac{1}{2}$
			$-\frac{1}{2}$
		1	$+\frac{1}{2}$
			$-\frac{1}{2}$
		0	$+\frac{1}{2}$
			$-\frac{1}{2}$
		-1	$+\frac{1}{2}$
			$-\frac{1}{2}$
		-2	$+\frac{1}{2}$
			$-\frac{1}{2}$
		-3	$+\frac{1}{2}$
			$-\frac{1}{2}$

Table 5 (completed)

Question 6

Answer   Copper is the second anomaly.

Comment

Using the rules and Figure 13 (c) you would expect

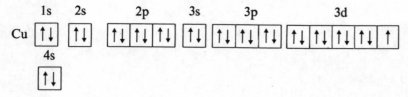

However, the possibility of filling the 3d sub-shell clearly must make the arrangement

more stable so the energy-level diagram is more complex than Figure 13 (c).

S.100—SCIENCE FOUNDATION COURSE UNITS